Warm Bodies

A NOVEL BY

DONALD R. MORRIS

DRAWINGS BY

FREDERICK E. BANBERY

SIMON AND SCHUSTER

NEW YORK: 1957

813
M66W

Browsing Room

To the Officer Detail Branch
of the Bureau of Naval Personnel,
without whose foresight
and long right arm
all this might have happened
on a battleship.

Warm Bodies

CHAPTER 1

THE Captain stepped to the railing outside the pilothouse and grasped it firmly with one hand. With the other, he fingered the leather strap of his binoculars. He glanced aft at the signal halyards, then into the pilothouse at the engine-order telegraph. The port engine indicated ahead full, the starboard engine back full. The rudder indicator was jammed hard against the starboard stops. He picked up his megaphone and turned toward the solitary officer visible on the conning tower of the other LST, perilously close in the gathering dusk. A sea gull wheeled over the mast and swooped down the narrow channel between the two ships. I held my breath.

"Now look what the hell you did," the Captain yelled through the megaphone.

The officer on the other ship turned toward us. He flicked his cigarette away and it fell between the two ships and hissed out on the wet concrete floor of the drydock.

"What did I do?" he asked suspiciously.

The Captain pointed at the floodlight illuminating the other ship's quarterdeck.

"You got your gangway light pointed right at my movie screen. We won't be able to see a damn thing."

"So move the screen. You shouldn't be showing movies topside this time of year anyway."

"Look, I got the screen rigged. I got all my chairs topside. I even got two projectors. I can't show below because I got wet paint on the tank deck. Just one little piece of cardboard over that light is all I'm asking. Now how about it?"

"Okay, O'Gara," the other officer said. "Okay. Anything for peace in the family."

The Captain looked around the drydock. The two LSTs were spotted well forward, hard against the caisson of the big dock in the Portsmouth Yard. Behind us, two smaller ships squatted on their keelblocks. To the right, across the low roof of a machine shop, the superstructure of a battleship serrated the evening sky. To the left, across more low roofs and the hammer head cranes, the lights of downtown

Norfolk were reflected by a low cloudbank. The wet floor of the drydock glistened below, where a few trapped fish still flapped in the puddles.

"Okay," the Captain said. "Let's eat."

The other officers were waiting in the wardroom. Schuyler Paffrath was a bachelor and our First Lieutenant, in that order. Our other ensign, Rudolph Rush, was married and the Operations Officer, also in that order. Murdoch Kutley was also married and was the Engineering Officer. The Captain, Bosworth O'Gara, was married and had three children. His family lived in Montana and he was, consequently, the only married man aboard who was apt to be taken for a bachelor, in that he was known to spend free evenings on the ship. I was the Executive Officer. I was also a bachelor. This was not entirely my own choice. I was perfectly willing to get married, but I had never been on a ship that stayed in one port long enough to do anything about it, except Norfolk, and I just hadn't found anyone in Norfolk.

Murdoch looked up. "Captain, the yard people say no work tomorrow. Christmas. Day after, all jobs start, except the soft-drink machine. They turned that one down again."

The Captain sat down at the head of the table and the rest of us took our places. The Captain picked up a spoon, leaned forward, and inspected the soup closely. He put the spoon down again.

"Vlasser back yet? What did he get?"

"He's bringing them now, Captain," Rudolph answered.

From somewhere aft the music of "Jingle Bells" wafted into the wardroom, borne on a lethargic current of moist air already heavily laden with the odor of baked beans. The wardroom door slammed, muting the music but having little effect on the beans, and Vlasser, the Movie Orderly, laid three movie folders in front of the Captain.

O'Gara picked them up, glanced at the titles.

"Two saddle jobs and *Gunga Din*. Vlasser, this is Christmas Eve. No pretty color? No Rita Hayworth? No happy songs?"

"Four cans just got in from the Med, Cap'n. They rate. I was lucky I got *Gunga Din*, they tole me."

"What's that one you're holding?"

"You don't wanna see that one, Cap'n."

"Gimme."

The Captain turned to the mimeographed review slip and read aloud.

"The life of a Kentucky Derby winner, from the time he is foaled until the day of the big race, as seen through the eyes of the horse."

O'Gara picked up his spoon again and sucked at it ruminatively. Then he tentatively shoved one of the Western folders forward.

Vlasser shrugged. "You da boss, Cap'n." He picked up all four folders and left.

The record was broken and "fannybrightmissfannybrightmissfannybright" shouldered the beans aside. The door slammed and the Captain mournfully inspected the bowl of the spoon he had been licking.

"Christmas Eve. Hell of a Christmas."

Schuyler started off casually. "If you left, say about eight, you could still catch that hop we set up for you. Be in Montana for dinner tomorrow night."

The Captain didn't say anything. He was squinting into the bowl.

"We can hold the fort down for ten days or so, sir," Murdoch volunteered.

O'Gara scratched his ear vigorously.

Rudolph tried a flanking attack.

"Anything particular you want to see before you shove off?"

The Captain rotated the spoon and inspected the back of it.

It was time to throw in the Old Guard.

"Garfield's back from leave," I remarked quietly.

The spoon clattered into the soup.

"He is? He is? Everything all right?"

I nodded.

"He came aboard right after we docked. Came right to the ship from the airport, never stopped in town. Quarter-deck Watch said he wanted to see *Gunga Din*."

The Captain leaned back in his chair and smiled at the handle of his spoon. Suddenly he turned to me.

"Say, I better get cracking if I want that ride, huh?"

I looked noncommittal.

"Sure you can trust us with the ship, sir?"

"Sure, sure. No reason for *me* to stick around. You're all big boys now. Besides, I'll be back before we're out of the dock. You're on ice, can't get into trouble *here*." He laughed.

We all laughed.

"I'll go pack." O'Gara got up and left the wardroom.

Schuyler looked around. "Let's see, now. That makes you acting skipper, doesn't it?"

"That's right," I answered.

"So you won't be standing in-port watches, huh?"

"I guess not."

"And *I've* got three days' leave, starting tonight. So which one of you two lucky bastards has the duty tomorrow?"

As much of the spirit of Christmas as had filtered through to the wardroom evaporated, with audible side effects. Rudolph Rush looked startled and turned ashen. Murdoch Kutley turned ashen and looked startled. Rudolph stared at Murdoch. Murdoch stared at me.

"Who, us?" they both asked.

"Why don't you flip for it?" I asked sweetly.

Murdoch put his hand in his pocket. There was a muted jingling. "No change," he said briefly.

"I will be happy," Schuyler said, "to lend you gentlemen a small coin."

He put a dime on the table.

Rudolph inspected it without touching it.

Murdoch reached out, turned it over, and looked at the other side. The wardroom door banged open and the Captain came in. He had his overcoat on and was carrying a small brown suitcase.

"Jingle bells, jingle bells, jingle all the way," he warbled happily. "I told the Quarterdeck to change the movie. *Gunga Din*, in twenty minutes. Jeep's coming for me right away. You sure you boys are going to be all right?"

"Captain," Schuyler said, "you catch that ride and forget all about this bucket. You've been pushing this ship all over the Atlantic, six months now. You haven't seen Mrs. O'Gara since July. You haven't seen the kids since the baby started to kindergarten. You go home and have a nice Christmas and you send us a postcard. We'll keep shop for you till you get back. Best-looking LST in Phiblant. We promise."

The Captain smiled. "Oh, I'm going to miss you bastards."

"We're going to miss you too, Captain," Rudolph said, choking.

A jeep honked. The Captain looked touched. He shook hands with all of us and started for the quarterdeck.

"Bosworth O'Gara," Murdoch said, "is probably the only skipper in this entire Navy who takes five in-port watches a week. Now he walks out on us on Christmas Eve. On ten minutes' notice. Look at him, all hot to trot."

Schuyler squinted at him. "Murdoch, when was the last time you spent a night on this ship in port?"

Murdoch considered. "October," he ventured. "Late October."

Schuyler made a rude noise.

Murdoch reconsidered.

"I *know* I took a watch in September."

"*I'll* take it tomorrow, Murdoch," Rudolph broke in. "I haven't stood one since August."

"Rudolph, you have a wife and son," Murdoch protested. "I only have a wife. I'll take it."

"As acting Captain of this ship," I announced, "I am now responsible for morale. Everybody's. Even mine. The thought of either one of you two slobs spending Christmas on this ship is more than my morale could stand. Beat it, both of you."

Rudolph and Murdoch smiled weakly, got up, and left the wardroom.

"You're chicken," Schuyler said without expression.

I squirmed. "It *is* Christmas. I'm a bachelor," I said in self-defense.

"Chicken."

"Okay. So I'm chicken."

One of the items no one ever seems to consider in choosing a naval career is that someone has to stay aboard in port, and on small ships the burden on junior officers is apt to be heavy. Until about the outbreak of the Second World War, the Navy found the idea of a junior officer being married a preposterous one, and if the Navy Department didn't put obstacles in the path of true love, it certainly didn't work very hard at removing any that already existed. (The British solved the problem very neatly by simply not paying anybody enough to support a wife until he got to be a commander—a system they have yet to change.) The theory was that a junior officer simply couldn't care for a wife and his professional duties to boot, and from the Navy's point of view it was a perfectly sound idea.

On every ship, accordingly, the schedules of duties was not only designed to fit the professional capabilities of the men but frequently had to take into account the marital status of the officers as well. Our In-Port Watch Bill illustrated this nicely. The Captain was never officially on the Watch Bill, and the Executive Officer didn't have to be, although I left myself on anyway. This meant that Schuyler, Rudolph, Murdoch and I in theory took the watches in turn, with weekends counting as one day. In practice, the Captain took the watch almost every night, except Thursdays, when he went downtown, called Montana, drank two beers, ate a chow mein dinner, and returned to the ship by ten o'clock, when he would relieve whichever one of us had the duty. Schuyler and I, of course, would stay aboard if we couldn't get ashore by, say, eight o'clock, but Murdoch or Rudolph would be off like a shot if relieved any time before six in the morning.

In very few professions is the cleavage between bachelors and married men as deep as it is in the Navy. Bachelors find on their ships a nucleus for their lives; the ship is home to them and to it they return from a generally hostile world. They spend numerous evenings aboard, entirely of their own volition, and they are forever worrying about the drapes in the wardroom or the fact that Diesel oil is again leaking from the showers. They buy magazine subscriptions for the wardroom, including *Home Beautiful*, chivvy the Steward's Mates with recipes for bouillabaisse and baked Alaska, and arrange for armchairs at the evening movies. They return from liberty panting under the weight of rugs for their staterooms, and, if not headed off by the First Lieutenant, may even try to have wardroom country painted beige. They take a great interest in the ship's laundry, with emphasis on the wardroom napery, and like to arrange little ship's parties, featuring great quantities of salted nuts and secret recipes for nonalcoholic punch. They have a fine disdain for the married men, who, they feel, are a bunch of insensitive louts with no interest in the habitability aspects of the wardroom.

In this they are frequently right. The married officers, for their part, look on the ship as a sort of office in which a certain amount of time must be spent daily before they are at liberty to return home. When they report aboard new ships and are shown their quarters, they sling their gear (and they have *much* less gear than bachelors do) onto the first vacant bunk, nod appreciatively at the cubicle to which they have been assigned (after all, they aren't really going to *live* there) and accept as settled all rooming arrangements, with at most a single remark: "Swell. Where's the john?"

Since it is necessary to obtain the permission of the Executive Officer before going ashore, married officers are exceptionally industrious during working hours. By liberty call there must be no unfinished business that would delay them for even a single instant. For this reason, married officers are much sought after for administrative posts and can be relied on implicitly to maintain a shipshape office. Married Executive Officers, who have to get the Captain's permission to go ashore, are in a class by themselves.

Every working day, on every Navy ship in port, at a quarter past four, the Boatswain's Mate of the Watch approaches the public-announcing system, takes a deep breath, blows a mellifluous blast on his little silver pipe,

· *11*

and passes the following word: "Now hear this. Knock off ship's work. Turn in all tools. Return all paint to the paint locker. Sweepers, man your brooms. Clean sweepdown, fore and aft. Sweep down all decks and ladders. The liberty party draw liberty cards and fall in on the quarterdeck for inspection." He repeats this twice.

The latter two-thirds of this announcement, and the fact that it is passed twice, constitute a mystery to many married officers, for somewhere between the "Knock off ship's work" and the business about the paint they have all appeared on the quarterdeck like magic. The rest of the announcement is drowned in the rumble of their passage down the gangway. Every last living one of them is armed with a treasured article, a small brown suitcase into which they have stuffed shaving kits, laundry, and socks with holes in them. By the end of the announcement they have disappeared up the piers and into the waiting automobiles, and the Navy knows them no more until the very last instant before liberty expires in the morning. At that time the Boatswain's Mate of the Watch will blow another blast and pass: "Now hear this. Quarters. All hands, fall in at Quarters. Divisional Officers, make your muster report to the Executive Officer on the quarterdeck." He will repeat this twice too, but again the repetition is a mystery, because the married officers, their little brown suitcases now stuffed with clean laundry and darned socks, do not arrive until the announcement is almost over, and some of them are still carrying their suitcases when they report to the

Executive Officer. For this reason, all married officers are known as "Brown Baggers."

When a Brown Bagger is finally cornered and handed the night's duty in port, the wardroom grows tense with emotion. Captain Dreyfus, departing for Devil's Island, could not have taken the coming separation from his family any harder. The approaching duty is a subject of conversation for days in advance. The man's home is reported as well stocked with food supplies, as if for a long siege. The radio, the TV set, and the phonograph have been inspected and adjusted. Detailed instructions have been left as to how to reach the police, the fire department and the ship.

On the inevitable night, the unhappy wretch may ask his wife aboard for dinner, and the two of them sit in the wardroom with mournful faces, forming a gauntlet through which bachelor officers must run on their way ashore. New officers, unaware of the nature of the trap, sometimes stop for a few minutes of friendly conversation. They are lost. At once they are plunged into heart-rending tales, told with a brave face, of the high cost of baby-sitters, of old friends in town just for the night, of aged parents being neglected, or of tickets for the Ballet Russe's last night in town which must now be abandoned. The officer who can take more than four minutes of this without breaking down and offering to take the Brown Bagger's duty is a rare one, and it is generally a good six months before he learns the formula: "I'll be back kind of early. May stand by for you then." It is at least a year before he learns that the safest course is simply "Hi, Pat. Lester. How's it going?" and then getting the hell off the ship before the answer starts.

Rudolph Rush was a particularly pathetic case. He had difficulty getting baby-sitters because he had no TV set, and since Rudolph Rush II, aetat three and a half, was straight out of Charles Addams, the baby-sitters he did get not only never came back, they warned off all their friends for a radius of seventeen miles. As a consequence, Rudolph not only had to bring his wife aboard for dinner, he also had to bring Rudolph II. The first time he did this, Schuyler, in a moment of weakness, offered to stand by for him. (It was a Thursday, and the Captain was ashore.) Rudolph and Elvira were off the ship so fast that it was a full fifteen minutes before Schuyler realized that Rudolph II had been entrusted to him until midnight, when Rudolph and Elvira were to come back to pick him up.

Neither Schuyler nor the ship remained quite the same after that evening. The duty Steward's Mate, a treasure whom we regarded as a lead-pipe cinch to re-enlist aboard, not only did not re-enlist aboard, he left the Navy. Rudolph II fell overboard twice, once carrying the ship's logbook, punched the General Alarm three times, managed to lower the forward end of the LCVP in the starboard davits (this usually took seven men and a Boatswain's Mate to tend the requisite lines), got loose on the bridge, where he turned on the breakdown lights and sounded the whistle and then locked himself in the radio shack and sang "Frère Jacques" on the Harbor Administrative Net for eighteen minutes, while naval activities as far away as Key West were aroused and Schuyler was breaking the door down with his bare fists and a small fire extinguisher.

When Rudolph I finally returned, three men were guarding Rudolph II on the quarterdeck and he was passed down so fast it was almost an hour before anyone noticed that the Duty Officer's .45 was missing. Rudolph I brought it back in the morning, with all the ammunition except one cartridge he said Rudolph II had swallowed, but it was months before Schuyler would speak to him again.

On overseas tours, the Brown Baggers form a pathetic group. Their little suitcases gather dust in their staterooms and they themselves sit around the wardroom in depressed, forlorn clusters. They spend every spare waking minute in an exhaustive analysis of the entire flow of naval communications, attempting to determine the exact date of their ship's return. The fact that a single destroyer, operating in the Persian Gulf, has been transferred for administrative reasons from Division 24 to Division 22 will be picked at for days, until every possible ramification of the transfer, and its possible effect on the duration of their own tour in the Caribbean, has been thoroughly explored. They subscribe to the *Congressional Record* and the *Army-Navy Times* and follow everything that might bear on ships' movements like so many beady-eyed vultures.

Their mail from home is filled with the same sort of information. They will spend hours weighing the relative merits of two rumors, one acquired at the dental clinic in Washington from the wife of a yeoman who is working in the Pentagon, and the other culled from an almost illegible note received by the ship's cook from a friend who sat behind what he thinks was a vice-admiral on a bus.

Ashore overseas, they shop. After a call at Bremerhaven, four-hundred-day clocks litter the staterooms; one day's liberty in Bizerte and it is impossible to move three feet on the ship without tripping over a camel saddle. Bosworth O'Gara was a particularly difficult man to shop with. I once spent an afternoon in a toy shop in Naples with him, where he finally made his wants clear to the proprietor. He wanted three toys, all alike to prevent civil warfare, but in different colors to aid identification. The toys couldn't be made of plastic, because the dog ate that, and his eldest child was allergic to feathers. He also didn't want to spend more than ten dollars. He finally settled for models of Vesuvius that squirted out puffs of talcum powder when you squeezed a concealed bulb.

When the ship finally does start for home, a new spirit moves through the ranks of the Brown Baggers. Speed, echoes the watch. The Navy, in its infinite wisdom, has decreed that about fifteen knots is a reasonable speed of advance for ships on the way home, what with the cost of fuel oil and all. If the Captain or the Executive Officer is a Brown Bagger, this is apt to be exceeded a bit. "Just adding a few turns for the foul bottom," the Captain says as he cranks on three full knots. All ships have to conduct at least one full power trial a year; no such trial has ever been held heading *away* from a home port. The trial lasts four hours, but it usually takes a day or so to build up speed and a day or two to reduce after the trial. Ships have been known to arrive in Norfolk four days early after sending "Increasing speed to avoid heavy weather" shortly after transiting Gibraltar.

The Engineering Officer is suddenly a friend, a close comrade. Good old Murdoch. Officers who have spent most of the trip making snide remarks about the dearth of hot water can now be found listening respectfully to long accounts of the Diesel lubrication system. The news that a

bearing is hotting up immediately has the wardroom cluttered with blueprints and engineering texts, while the more naïve souls descend to the shaft alleys with ice bags.

The Executive Officer loses the few friends he has left. On his desk for some time now have been three piles of paper. One of these represents ship's work which is to be accomplished when the ship gets back. The second pile is a series of orders detailing various people, invariably key members of their departments, to school. The third pile, which is by far the largest, consists of leave requests. There will come a night, shortly before the ship's arrival, when the Executive Officer will not be seen at dinner, nor will he be seen at the movies. The ship's office will be open until the small hours, and woe unto him who ventures in without sufficient reason. In the morning, the Executive Officer will be unshaven and grim, and in the midship's passage will be posted the leave list, to which is appended a notice in underlined red capitals that absolutely no requests for modifications will be considered. The list will be modified at least eight times before noon.

The final moments before docking are an agony. If the trip has been a long one, the line handlers on the dock stumble around in a dense throng of what the Navy Department refers to as "dependents." Port Control has great difficulty reading the ship's semaphore through the forest of waving arms. Small brown suitcases, sitting next to four-hundred-day clocks, can be encountered discreetly hidden in a number of strategic locations. The owners of the bags can be found by drawing a line from the quarterdeck through the bag and extending it.

The story is still told, of Lieutenant Thrushkin, Gunnery Officer of the old four-piper *Poundstone*. The *Poundstone* was entering San Diego harbor at ten o'clock on a sunny August morning some twenty years ago, after eighteen months in China. While still two hundred yards from Broadway Pier, and long before any one else had tried to bridge the narrowing gap of water with vocal greetings, Thrushkin looked up from the forecastle and spotted his wife in a large group of people waiting at the end of the pier.

"Hiya, honey!" he bellowed into the stillness. "Sleepy?"

Vlasser came into the wardroom. "Movie whenever you're set, sir."

Schuyler looked up. "*Gunga Din*, of course?"

Vlasser nodded.

"Fine, fine. We haven't had that since—let's see, about last Thursday, wasn't it?"

"About that." Vlasser left, and Schuyler turned to me.

"It might pay to get a permanent copy of that picture for the ship. Save us a lot of leg work."

We went up to the main deck, pulling on foul-weather

jackets. Just before the lights were doused, I turned around and looked over the audience. The entire duty section was present, except for the Quarterdeck Watch and the Cold Iron Watch in the engineering spaces. In the middle of the audience, seated on a folded blanket and smiling happily up at the screen, was Garfield. He saw me, and the smile widened to include gleaming teeth which flashed as the lights flickered out.

Garfield—Shrieking Eagle Garfield, Seaman Apprentice, 122 25 32, United States Navy—was our problem child, and we had long been resigned to the fact that the problem was apparently an insoluble one. Shrieking Eagle had enlisted the day after Pearl Harbor and had not been promoted since he left recruit training. Rank *per se* did not interest him, and he never drew any pay anyway, because he was rich—stinking rich. Whenever he needed money, he just sent a telegram to his father, Black Gold Garfield, or to one of his uncles, Gushing Garfield or Options Garfield, and in a little while a money order would come which could be cashed in the city. Telegrams could be dictated, and Shrieking Eagle regarded this process as much simpler than filling out Navy pay chits, which not only had to be dated but also had to have the amount desired written out twice, in figures and in script, and further required him to list his rank and serial number and ship, fingerprint the result, and then wait in a line until the paymaster got around to the "G" 's. The bi-weekly pay list got to be a big joke on our ship.

French, H. S.	SA	215 38 64	$49.00
Gaines, W. L.	SN	314 32 52	$72.00
Garfield, S. E.	SA	122 25 32	$12,897.00
Garlinghouse, B. A.	QM3	356 75 45	$91.00

Shrieking Eagle would have been discharged long ago, for inaptitude, except that within a fortnight of his arrival on any given ship it would invariably be discovered that he was not only not inapt but literally indispensable. Shrieking Eagle was a natural born boatswain, a man who could singlehandedly rig, operate and repair deck gear that could reduce grizzled chief petty officers to tears. When a ship was scheduled to refuel at sea, any Boatswain's Mate worth his salt would have the entire Deck ▮▮▮ up long before dawn, breaking out, sorting, and setting up the required welter of lines, snatch-blocks, hoses, flags, sound-powered telephones, and tools. Shrieking Eagle, with two green men to help him, could start the process about the time the ship was making its approach on the oiler, and be ready and paring his palms with a sheath knife when the first line came across from the tanker. It was the same story with the ground tackle. The Garfield Flying Moor was never officially adopted by the Navy because no one could reduce it to paper or explain it to anyone else, but it was used with great success on every ship Shrieking Eagle ever served in.

I had three times attempted to administer a Seaman's examination to him, but I finally had to admit defeat. No matter how simple the questions were (and the last examination had been downright puerile), Shrieking Eagle always followed the same procedure. He would write his name at the top of the examination, turn the paper over, and start to copy the opening lines of "Hiawatha," continuing until he ran out of paper or we called time. This virtuosity had apparently served to graduate him from whatever educational system he had originally been inflicted on, and he saw no reason to change it now. For some time we had been nerving ourselves to give him an examination simply reading, "Write down as much as you remember of 'Hiawatha,'" but since the new Division Commander personally inspected all the examinations, we never quite dared.

What really made Shrieking Eagle an alloy to the ship was that about once a quarter he went ashore. On these rare occasions even married officers had been known to remain aboard voluntarily until he was returned to the ship. This usually happened before midnight. His annual leave wasn't so bad, because whatever happened happened in Oklahoma, where Black Gold or Options or Gushing could deal with him. In Norfolk, however, the situation was chancy, because the Shore Patrol had never been able to locate anyone who spoke Chickasaw, which was all Shrieking Eagle would use when he was upset. Schuyler had been an anthropology major at Columbia, and he finally wrote one of his former professors for a short list of simple commands in Chickasaw. This list we mimeographed and distributed to the various Shore Patrol stations. It helped a little, but even in Chickasaw there was a limited amount that could be done with Shrieking Eagle.

One night in October Shrieking Eagle wandered into a theater in Portsmouth, where a three-dimensional picture was being shown. He spurned the proffered spectacles and seated himself in the third row. This was during the newsreel. About three minutes after the main feature started he politely yelled "Focus!" When a repeated request drew no result, except for some muttering from the people seated in his immediate vicinity, he clambered up to the stage and slit the screen from one side to the other with his sheath knife. He then delivered a harangue to the projection booth, in Chickasaw, which the Shore Patrol had been unable to halt for some time after its arrival because the officer in charge of the patrol couldn't find "Come down" on his list, and the anthropologist who had drawn up the list had unfortunately used what turned out to be the intransitive infinitive instead of the imperative form of the verb "stop."

This eventually cost Shrieking Eagle close to a thousand dollars, including reimbursing all the tickets, and we got another direct order from the Type Commander to court-martial him. He got off scot-free, as usual, because Black Gold's lawyers, who flew in from Tulsa, by this time knew much more about the Uniform Code of Military Justice than any legal talent our ship was able to produce. The first court-martial the ship had held on Shrieking Eagle (for tearing the license plate off a commander's car that honked at him while he was crossing Hampton Boulevard) had gone clear up to the Pentagon before resulting in an acquittal. For about a month Shrieking Eagle kept the lawyers in town, lending them to friends of his, and hardly a ship or station in the Hampton Roads area got a conviction during the entire period. Finally, with the future of naval discipline hanging in the balance, Options drove a Cadillac into a hotel lobby and all the lawyers had to fly back to Oklahoma. They had been back to Norfolk eight times since then, and officially Shrieking Eagle still had a virgin conduct sheet.

He once put in for a week's leave on the grounds that he was needed at home to open the annual Rain Ceremony. I turned this down. Three days later the ship got a dispatch from the Secretary of the Navy, stating that both the Secretary of the Interior and the Secretary of Health, Education and Welfare were interested in the case, and two admirals and a congressman visited the ship personally. Shrieking Eagle left in a huff and it rained the entire nine days he was gone.

Since then I had gotten on extremely well with him. I think he liked me because I could say "Let go of him" in Chickasaw. He *had* smiled at me just then, but, even so, it was almost ten weeks since our final conference with the theater manager and it was just a question of time now.

The picture ground on. The crew knew most of the dialogue by heart by this time, and repeated it along with the players. At intervals Shrieking Eagle's rich, hearty laughter boomed out over the audience. The picture finished, the deck lights came on, and the crew got up stiffly. The Quarterdeck Watch passed "Tattoo" over the P.A. system, and the men dispersed, calling out "Merry Christmas" to us and to each other as they went below.

Schuyler and I went back to the wardroom.

"I'll catch the midnight bus," Schuyler said, pouring us out some coffee.

"This is the third Christmas running I've had the duty," I said glumly.

"It's your own fault. You should get married. Brown Baggers never have the duty Christmas. They practically never have the duty ever. Look at Rudolph. Look at Murdoch."

"*You're* no Brown Bagger. The only holiday you ever spent on this ship was Simon Bolivar's birthday. Two years ago."

"That's different," Schuyler said loftily.

"How come it's different?"

"Well, it just is. I happen to have leave."

"You *always* have leave."

Schuyler stirred his coffee. In those circles concerned with the career analysis of naval officers, Schuyler had long ago been written off as a possible future Chief of Naval Operations. There were even those who had their doubts about his making lieutenant (junior grade). This bothered Schuyler not a whit, and he continued to function effectively as an LST's First Lieutenant.

After he graduated from Columbia, he had started his career in Public Information, which was always on the make for fresh talent. His first assignment had been to a carrier, and he had proven invaluable. Schuyler could take a story—any story—and clothe it in a smooth prose that delighted the battered ears of admirals. Off Korea, the pilot of a propeller-driven attack plane had tangled with a MIG in an area where MIGs were a rarity, and had barely managed to get his riddled craft back to the carrier. Schuyler's story, with the report that "at medium altitudes, the terminal velocity characteristics of the current Soviet reaction-engine production fighter compare favorably with, if they do not in fact exceed, similar characteristics of the current American attack production model" was a far cry from the statement "the son of a bitch went by so fast I never even saw him," which was all that debriefing could wring from the flustered pilot. Similarly, his "the prevailing meteorological phenomena, ranging from marginal to unacceptable, eventually forced the strike group leader to seek out secondary objectives to fulfill his assigned mission" was based on "I couldn't find the goddam bridge so I dumped 'em in the ocean."

Schuyler did so well on the carrier that he was sent back to the Pentagon, apparently slated for a meteoric rise in Public Information. In the Pentagon he lasted four weeks.

He had been assigned the task of writing captions for the daily stack of photographs arriving from Korea. In his third week, he gradually became aware of the fact that nine out of every ten photographs featured the activities of a group of congressmen touring the neutral zone at Panmunjom. The congressmen were photographed with admirals, with generals, with interpreters, and with pretty Red Cross workers. They were photographed getting into helicopters and getting out of jeeps. They were photographed standing on trucks and sitting under tents. Schuyler finally found a photograph of a group of the barrage balloons used to mark off the neutral zone. The balloons were inflated, but still tethered to the ground, just before being raised on their cables, and they dotted a hillside across a little valley. Schuyler turned the photograph over and wrote across the back, "Bending over to tie their shoelaces, the congressmen snatch a moment's relaxation during their recent tour of the neutral zone." Schuyler then went to lunch, and his yeoman typed the captions without looking at the pictures. Schuyler was removed from caption writing and set to checking press releases for punctuation.

In three days he was in the soup again. A commander was being transferred at the end of a normal three-year tour, and because he had been a very co-operative commander, some of the newspaper boys gave a party for him, complete with skits and a few fake press releases. One of these releases drifted back to the office the next day, and because the punctuation was in perfect order, Schuyler stamped it and sent it down to the press room. That afternoon the local papers dutifully reported that "Commander Eccles, of the Office of Public Information, is being transferred to Pearl Harbor upon completion of his tour in the Pentagon. Commander Eccles was noted for the care with which he investigated each press query, having once delayed the Associated Press four months, two weeks and three days checking on the question 'Is Admiral Bass in this morning?'"

Shortly after he arrived in Kabul, Schuyler came down with what was finally diagnosed as acute camel mange, the first recorded case in a human being since 1878. He spent three months in Bethesda and then joined us.

He finished his coffee and left the wardroom. A few minutes later he came by again with a small brown suitcase, stuck his head in, and waved goodbye.

"Brown Bagging, huh?" I asked.

Schuyler looked at the suitcase. "Murdoch's," he said. "He has two."

He waved again and left.

The ship was quiet, with only the dim background hum of our generators breaking the stillness. Outside, I heard the Quarterdeck Watch stamp his feet. On every Navy ship, I thought, all over the world, there is someone on the quarterdeck stamping his feet. I was not alone.

It was a comforting thought.

CHAPTER 2

CHRISTMAS morning was clear and crisp and not too cold. Lownes, the Steward's Mate, served me breakfast in the wardroom and I took stock. The prospect of a full day as the only officer aboard a ship in drydock is never a pleasant one. The prospect on Christmas is downright discouraging. Since a full third of the crew is in a similar position, each ship makes every effort to provide what it can in the way of seasonal cheer.

No Navy ship is really designed with festivities in mind, and celebrating a holiday presents certain difficulties. In

the matter of decorations, the Christmas spirit was represented by a large evergreen bough sprouting from the
radar antenna and a small tree with colored lights wired
to the top of the conning tower.

We were too small to have a chaplain of our own, but
the battleship in the next drydock had promised to lend
us one in the evening. In the meantime, a few men at a
time could be released to attend services at the base chapel.

We once had a chaplain, but he only stayed three days
and then left us for a cruiser. He said we weren't ready
to have a chaplain yet.

Father Slifer had been a very nice man, and a conscien-
tious one, but his major difficulty had been that nothing in
his background had prepared him for duty on an LST.
The day he came aboard he had informed the yeoman that
he would celebrate Mass in the wardroom every afternoon
at 1600, and would the yeoman please make a note in the
Plan of the Day. The next Plan of the Day came out with
the following addition:

1500	Request Mast
1530	Disciplinary Mast
1600	Catholic's Mast

Nobody came except Shrieking Eagle, who was very
religious. He was a shaman himself, and he attended all
the services that were ever scheduled as a matter of professional courtesy. This made Father Slifer very nervous,

for Shrieking Eagle always muttered his prayers in Chickasaw, and nobody ever knew to Whom or What they were being muttered.

Shrieking Eagle was regularly converted every few months or so, and would be almost as difficult to handle during the process as when his father's lawyers were in town. For a fortnight after Billy Graham visited Norfolk, Shrieking Eagle used to grab the P.A. system at odd hours, generally in the middle of the night, and preach to the crew in Chickasaw. Once we failed an important Fueling-at-Sea exercise because he refused to work on Yom Kippur. After Father Slifer had been aboard one day, Shrieking Eagle took a shine to him and showed unmistakable signs of being ripe for conversion again, and Father Slifer borrowed the mimeographed sheet and spent most of the night trying to translate the Shorter Catechism into Chickasaw. He wasn't very happy with the result in the morning. He couldn't understand what the Anthropology Department at Columbia was up to, with phrases like "Drop that," "Put (him) (her) (it) down gently," and "Come out with your hands up."

Just before supper a seminary friend of his came aboard. The friend was assigned to a Marine unit and Father Slifer discussed with him the advisability of transferring from the LST. The friend was horrified.

"Don't you do it," he said. "You've got a great life here— magnificent opportunities. I'm positive I saw an aborigine on the main deck just now. You forget the Marine Corps;

all those marches! The last two services I held were eleven miles apart, in a swamp."

Father Slifer wasn't convinced and left the next day, anyway. Shrieking Eagle was heartbroken and didn't snap out of it until Ramadan.

On this particular Christmas, the ship's routine dispensed with reveille and then featured a gargantuan meal at noon, over which Gruber, the ship's cook, had been toil-

ing for two days. Navy chow was *always* good, and holidays called for an expansion in quantity rather than quality. I stuck my head into the galley and looked around. Gruber was riding herd on the turkeys in the oven and barking orders at the mess cooks, all of whom looked a bit frazzled but still in control of the situation. Gruber nodded at me and pointed at a pile of mimeographed menus on the chopping block. I picked one up.

SOUP DE JOUR

ROAST TOM TURKEY

SAUCE GRUBER

HAM WITH PINEAPPLES

ASPARAGUS

CANDIED SWEET POTATOES

MINCE PIE   CHERRY PIE   NO LEMON PIE, SORRY

CELERY   RADISHES   PICKLES   EASY ON THE RADISHES, NOW

NUTS, SOME SHELLED   ICE CREAM   LOTS OF CANDY

NOTE: THERE ARE SEVEN TURKEYS. THIS MEANS FOURTEEN DRUMSTICKS. DRUMSTICKS WILL BE DISTRIBUTED AS FOLLOWS:

WARDROOM 1

CHIEF POPPER 1

GRUBER 1

MESS COOKS 3

THIS LEAVES EIGHT. FIRST COME FIRST SERVED.

A MOVIE WILL BE SHOWN IN AFTER CREW'S QUARTERS AFTER THE MEAL. THE MOVIE WILL NOT START UNTIL THE MESS HALL HAS BEEN SWABBED DOWN. THERE WILL BE NO EVENING CHOW. LEFTOVERS ON REQUEST AT THE GALLEY, WHILE THEY LAST.

"Looks great," I said. "What's this Sauce Gruber?"

"My girl give it to me. It's for the asparagus. What's this tarragon crap she's talking about?"

"You're the cook, Gruber. Better put it in a bowl. The boys can help themselves."

Gruber could be trusted, and he was trusted—by every bachelor on the ship. His chow was adequate, hot, and always served on time. Even so, Gruber had trouble with the Brown Baggers.

If I may be allowed a digression (and since I'm telling this story you'll have to bear with me), the subject of cookery will serve as well as any other to bring home the depths of the chasm separating the bachelors from the Brown Baggers.

Navy bachelors have an entirely subjective approach to cooking: they eat. They eat what is put before them, and, since someone is usually waiting for their place at the table, they eat in a hurry. It is possible, although highly unlikely, to develop a palate aboard ship, but the entire tradition of the sea is against it. Navy bachelors go through life putting up with endless culinary barbarities; fortified behind a screen of ketchup, they wolf down their rations and consider themselves well fed. The galley is a sparkling place, to be inspected on Saturday mornings, when a small cake will be sliced and tactfully placed where the inspecting party can reach it on their way out. Gruber is a sterling fellow; was it not he who provided that steak sandwich after that last, wet midwatch? Bachelors have no standard of comparison, and, like the Soviet citizen, consider themselves better off than the rest of the world.

The bachelor has always taken his food as it comes. In childhood he was fed at home and took what he got for granted. In his first few days in the service he was too hungry at mealtimes to notice that what he was swilling down was not precisely up to Mama's popovers and fried chicken. Plentiful, substantial, sometimes even appetizing, but that *je sais quoi* was apt to be missing. By the time he had settled down into service life, he was habituated to service fare, and Mama's kitchen magic was a dim and pious memory. During leaves, he would be once again confronted with this magic, but three days after the leave was up he was once again snug in the wardroom and howling for more ketchup.

Even the blunted taste buds of the bachelors sometimes recalled that there were Better Things in Life. New mess treasurers, glowing with zeal, would lay in stocks of Westphalian ham, potted lobster, smoked oysters and exotic Danish cheeses, and the bachelors would point out to one another that there was nothing, but nothing, like good ole Navy chow. On pay day, when the mess bills were toted up, the new mess treasurer would look green and lose a biggish slice of his zeal, and there would be mutterings about "conservation" and "plain, *wholesome* fare." The loudest mutterer would be elected mess treasurer, the ketchup stains would appear again on the tablecloth, and the whole cycle would start over.

From these fluctuations the Brown Baggers remained serenely aloof. In port they would descend from a home breakfast of creamed codfish and shirred eggs to whatever the mess treasurer had picked for the noon meal, and the noon meal was the only meal the Brown Baggers usually had to deal with. Lunch therefore served as a standard of comparison for whatever the Little Lady wanted to dish up that evening, and some wives even drew attention to their virtuosity by consistently serving to their husbands *their* versions of what the louts had just had for lunch, with no complaints. A really good cook could keep this up for about ten days.

The Brown Baggers frequently pushed their advantage. Mess treasurers would be asked why didn't they try just a pinch of saffron in the rice, and sometimes there were even offers to have Elvira come down and show Gruber how stuffed peppers *ought* to be prepared. Some Brown Baggers even discussed the best wine years in the ward-room, a subject that left the average bachelor glowering.

I once had to cook for myself for an entire year, how-ever, and felt I could hold my own with the Brown Baggers. Assigned to duty in Washington, my orders had been stamped "No Government Quarters Available." It was ex-plained to me that I would be issued a special allowance and I would then be responsible for my own room and board. I was enchanted. Four hours later I was the pos-sessor, at an exorbitant rental, of a furnished efficiency apartment and a Pullman kitchenette containing every food-processing device known to man. The ad had stated "suitable for young diplomat," and diplomats were still in a respected profession in those days. The kitchenette was most impressive. A good cook with that layout could have gotten a French passenger liner halfway to Cherbourg without calling for help. At the moment, the only utensil I could identify with any degree of certainty was the frying pan (which turned out to be a skillet), but I made a bee-line for the neighborhood delicatessen, unloaded $32.07, and staggered back for my very first meal in my very own apartment. It was not a success.

To begin with, I thought the man behind the counter had said "boil 'er" instead of "broiler," and around ten o'clock I had to discard the chicken. Also, whatever you did to corn on the cob to get it hot, you didn't do it in a frying pan. I was learning, I told myself, opening a can of peaches.

During the next few weeks I learned a lot more. I even invented a dish, *œufs pèse-papier*, which is a sort of omelet that looks like a fried egg, on one side, with bananas. (I like bananas.) Except for the eggs, however, I didn't learn enough. A girl in the office where I was working heard I was cooking for myself and gave me a recipe that was supposed to be infallible. It was for something called "beer balls," and I was progressing swimmingly until I got to the word "marinate." The dictionary said "to let lie, in a brine or pickle." It didn't say for how long, and the brine didn't sound as if it would go with the beer. I did have a large pickle, however, so I hollowed it out and stuffed in as much of the meat as I could. Then I got to thinking about the pickle and the beer, and it didn't sound any better than the brine and the beer, so I threw out the pickle and just drank the beer.

I explained all this to the girl at the office and she shook her head and told me about "marinate" and gave me another recipe for something called "*pêche flambée*," which was like shish-kebab, only you used peaches instead of tomatoes. That one worked out smoothly until the very end, when I accidently set fire to the Venetian blinds over the kitchenette with one skewer while I was taking the other one out of the stove. I didn't notice it at first, because the water was running and I thought the smoke was coming from the oven, but someone across the street spotted it and turned in an alarm. When the Fire Department got there they said you couldn't possibly start a fire the way I said this one had started, and when I tried to show them they turned out to be right.

After that I gave up collecting advice and evolved my own system. To begin with, the number of dishes and utensils that got sullied and had to be cleaned in the preparation and consumption of one meal for one person was downright scandalous. I found out there were no less than eight varieties of canned beef stew on the market, so I made a stand out of a wire coathanger that held one can over the front burner. When the stew started to bubble I picked up the can with a potholder and ate the stew with a pair of chopsticks. The can could be cleaned out and used for instant coffee, the coathanger used again, and the chopsticks licked clean. From then on I hardly ever used a dish, and in the last five months I never had to wash a single piece of silverware.

After a while I branched out and started substituting lamb stew for beef stew. There were six varieties of lamb stew, and it made a nice change. Once in a while I just ate raw chopped meat, which didn't even get the chopsticks dirty.

Only once did the system break down. The girl in the office heard about the *œufs pèse-papier*, and with a horrified look offered to come up and prepare what she referred to as a decent meal for me. She gave me a tremendous list of things to get, all of which I got, except the soubise, which I went to seven stores to find and couldn't. When she showed up she spent one hour and forty-seven minutes in the kitchenette turning out one meal for two people. In the process she got every single pot, pan, and gadget I owned dirty, including three eggbeaters, and she burned herself twice and broke a chopstick. The meal wasn't particularly good, and it took me three hours to clean up afterward. One of the pots, the one she started the dessert in, still isn't clean.

Except for that episode, it was a most successful year, and I gained eight pounds. I was not prepared to take any guff off the Brown Baggers, and I felt a professional kinship with Gruber.

There was a matinee movie scheduled for Christmas Day, as well as the regular evening show. Vlasser had outdone himself. First, he had talked Shrieking Eagle out of wanting to see *Gunga Din* again, no mean feat in itself, and then he had traded the equine autobiography off to the other LST for a musical, only having to throw six gallons of white paint into the bargain.

There was to be no ship's party this year. Normally, the ship gave a Christmas party and, overseas, parties for local orphanages were always popular. This year, however, there weren't enough ship's children in Norfolk to make a party worth while, and, in addition, the Captain had become a little edgy about parties in general, ever since our last one, which had taken place in a small Italian port.

The local authorities had reported the existence of a deserving orphanage which would be likely to enjoy such a shindig, so we collected ice cream and cookies and lots of toys and enough cartoons for a one-hour show. We even ticked off a sailor to act as Big Brother for each orphan, so that no one would get lost or fall overboard or try to drop the anchor. At two o'clock, all the Big Brothers were on deck, looking a bit dispirited, and the Quarterdeck Watch was waiting for the busful of orphans to arrive. When it did arrive, a howl went up that brought everyone aboard running to the quarterdeck.

When I got there, the orphans were getting out of the bus and lining up in two rows by height. They were all female, and from the looks of things not a one was under

sixteen, even allowing for early Mediterranean development. All the Big Brothers were lining up by height, too, and jockeying for position, and a fight had already started because one Big Brother had bought out for five dollars and now wanted to buy back in for twenty and there were no takers. The two nuns in charge looked a bit apprehensive, which was nothing to the way Captain O'Gara looked. You couldn't tell where the khaki shirt left off and O'Gara started, until you got to teeth. He hastily ordered the ice cream and cake dispensing to be shifted from the tank deck to the middle of the main deck, where everyone would be in plain view, and canceled liberty for all the officers. It was too late to call off the movie, but an officer with a battlelight was stationed at each exit from the tank deck. Even so, it was some time after the movie was over before we could get the tank deck lights on again; we eventually found four short circuits.

When it was time to go, the nuns couldn't agree as to how many girls had come aboard, and one of them insisted two were missing. We immediately mustered the crew and found that Schuyler and Shrieking Eagle were absent, and by then *both* nuns were insisting that two girls were missing. We sent out search parties, and Captain O'Gara was pawing through a small English-Italian dictionary, and the nuns were yelping *"Prego!"* and grabbing for the Italian-English section, when the missing four turned up on the bridge, where they had been inspecting the ship.

All the girls lined up by height again and marched off

the ship, with the nuns on one side counting in Italian and Captain O'Gara on the other side counting in English and Shrieking Eagle at the foot of the gangway counting, we thought, in Chickasaw, until I realized he was only estimating bust measurements.

By eleven o'clock I was up in the sharply rising bows of the ship, making a final pre-dinner check. We were jammed against the caisson forming the gate of the drydock, so that the bows overhung the walkway across the top of it. Most of the crew was on deck, loitering in the vicinity of the chow line. From the galley came muted clashes and clangs, and every now and again a mess cook would emerge with a steaming covered tray, bark "Gangway! Hot stuff!", shoulder through the crowd and disappear below.

Out over the caisson lay the river, and, far beyond, the city of Norfolk. Sea gulls dipped and cried, and a small tug, with a man on the fantail faking down a line, chuffed down the river. One sea gull investigated the fantail, found it bare of edibles, and flapped up and away. I never could work up any enthusiasm over sea gulls. My ornithological classification abilities were limited to large birds, little brown birds, and owls. Sea gulls fell into the first category.

"Hello, there!"

It was a feminine voice. No one was in sight.

"Hello, up there!"

I leaned over the bows and looked down. Standing on the caisson and rapping on the overhanging bow doors with a shoe heel was a girl. She had red hair and blue eyes and she was wearing a green overcoat.

"Hi," I answered, after a while.

"I want to come aboard. May I?"

This struck me as a splendid idea.

"By all means. Have you had dinner?"

"No, I haven't. Not since last night."

"Then come and have Christmas dinner with me," I said. "We're having turkey," I added.

"How do I get up?"

I pointed.

"You walk around the edge of the dock to that ship there, and then you go across it. I'll meet you on our quarterdeck."

She nodded, smiled, and put the shoe back on. Then she started off. It was an enchanting smile. The ankle was nice, too.

"Don't stop on that other ship," I yelled after her. "Our turkey is much better." She turned around and nodded.

I watched until she reached the edge of the drydock and then dashed down to our quarterdeck and waited. The girl presently appeared on our neighbor's quarterdeck, electrifying the watch and the loiterers on *that* ship, crossed over it, and started across the brow to our ship. Someone yelled "Gangway! Hot stuff!" She ignored it.

She stepped aboard carefully, not tripping over the end of the brow the way most visitors do. We shook hands. At close range, her hair was even redder and her eyes were very blue and they went with the hair. She had one freckle, on the side of her nose, up high. After a moment or so she retrieved her hand and I showed her into the wardroom. I helped her out of her coat. There was a green dress under the coat and whoever had been yelling in the chow line knew what he was yelling about. I rang for Lownes, told him there would be two for dinner instead of one, and offered her a cigarette.

She introduced herself. Her name was Sally.

"I work for a newspaper. Are you the Captain?"

"Well, right now I am. What kind of a newspaper?" There had been this character a year or so back who spent three hours on the ship and then wrote an article called "Beneath Every White Hat a Broken Heart."

"A big newspaper, in New York. I want a story about what the Navy does on Christmas."

I waved a hand around the wardroom.

"We entertain. Open house. But nobody ever comes."

"*I* came. I want to know all about Christmas on a ship. I want a *good* story."

I considered this. I had been reading my share of newspapers and magazines lately, and as far as I could figure out the working press seemed to think the Navy consisted exclusively of frogmen, grounded battleships, and nuclear submarines. And except for the gentleman a year or so back, the only reporter we had ever seen was the man who came the time Shrieking Eagle held up the sailing of the

Kiptopeke Ferry one hour because a man in an Oldsmobile wouldn't salute the flag when he drove on board.

"Why us?" I asked at last. "There's a nice big battleship in the next drydock. We're small fry."

"I tried them. They have measles. No visitors. Besides, I want to write about a small ship."

"Where did you get this idea?"

"Well, normally I review children's books. For months now I've wanted to write a *story*. I studied journalism four years, and now all they let me write about is *The Wind in the Willows*. I've got two weeks' vacation and I'm on my way home to Little Hominy and I want to see the—"

"Where?"

"Little Hominy. It's in North Carolina. That's where I grew up."

"Hominy?"

"*Little* Hominy. You're probably confusing it with Big Hominy, but that's only the depot."

"Of course. Go on."

"I went to see the Managing Editor. I told him I wanted to write a story. He took me out to dinner. He was in the Navy during the war and he once spent Christmas on a minesweeper off a little island somewhere, and he's been sorry for the Navy ever since. He said, you're going South, so stop off in Norfolk and write me a story about the Navy and Christmas. Visit a ship. Write about it. About all those poor little bastards stuck with the duty. A great story, he said. Then he passed out."

"Your editor is a Brown Bagger," I said. She looked puzzled. I explained. She pulled out a little notebook and scribbled industriously with a red pencil.

"More," she said. "Tell me about the ship. What kind of a ship is this, anyway?"

I told her.

We were an LST, I told her, and officially it stood for Landing Ship, Tank. Sometimes, in heavy weather, Lousy Stinking Tub would be bruited about, but it usually stopped when the sun came out. The British had the idea for LSTs first, they were only supposed to go short distances carrying all sorts of military goodies. After they were built, however, they came out so big it seemed a shame not to make them fully oceangoing, so the Navy tacked a radar set on, added a small conning tower to the original shielded wheel, and enlarged the icebox. We didn't go very fast, but we almost always got there eventually, and when we did we could run right up on the beach and dump our load in the laps of the Marine Corps.

Sally was scribbling all this down, so I expanded.

During the war, the Amphibious Service was known as the Hooligan Navy. Before anyone in Washington could yell "Whoa!" there were over a thousand LSTs alone, not to mention LCTs, LCI(L)s, LSMs, LSMRs, and LSDs. Lots and lots of men were needed in amphibs, and the leaven of regulars was worked even thinner than it was elsewhere. The people who wound up in amphibs were only interested in getting the war over and done with, and they paid even less attention to paperwork and paint and uniforms than anyone else. Since the Hooligan Navy was doing an outstanding job, nobody bothered them much and they wore their sobriquet with a raffish pride. After the war, the people left in amphibs were a little dismayed to find out that the Hooligan Navy was no longer expected to be raffish but was now supposed to develop an *esprit de corps* similar to that, say, of the Destroyer Force.

This proved to be difficult. In the first place, destroyers bristled with guns and torpedoes and dashed around at thirty-one knots and looked nautical as all get-out. LSTs had to be inspected very closely before you could see any guns at all (although they had been used very effectively when the occasion demanded), and they all looked like shoeboxes with the mast in the wrong place. When two of them passed each other at top speed in opposite directions they were still considerably short of mustering thirty-one knots between them. We did have a Lieutenant known as "Damn the torpedoes, all ahead one third—no, I guess maybe you'd better back her down" Copeland, and then there were special amphibious types like Shrieking Eagle. So, all in all, we did have a flavor of our own.

Then I showed Sally the ship. It *was* almost exactly like a shoebox, with most of the important things stuck into the tail end. Up forward the shoebox was open, with a ramp and bow doors to close the box. When we ran up on a beach we opened the doors and let down the ramp and whatever was in the box could run right off the tank deck out onto the beach. The main deck back to the super-structure was flat and empty, and right aft of the anchors was a big elevator connecting the main deck with the tank deck so everything on the main deck could go down and run out the bow doors too.

Aft on the main deck was the superstructure, with officers' quarters and the galley. On top of that was a three-story structure where the pilot house, the captain's sea cabin and the conning tower were piled on top of each other, with a signal deck on the same level as the sea cabin. Back of all these was our mast, and back of the mast was the stern-anchor winch, which helped to get us off beaches, sometimes.

Visitors always wanted to see the conning tower, which sounded very dramatic. On most ships it was. On a destroyer, for example, the conning tower was simply crammed chockful of esoteric gear. In addition to the wheel and the engine-order telegraphs, radar scopes overlapped sonar scopes, and there were telephones and announcing systems and squawk boxes and handles and lights and mysterious switch boxes and banks of voice tubes wherever you looked. The navigator had a nice big table and the captain had a nice big table and a special armchair and there were heaters near both of them and windshield wipers on the portholes.

Our conning tower measured six feet by six feet and had a gyro repeater to take bearings and a voice tube. Depending on how loudly you yelled into the voice tube, you could get Captain O'Gara in his sea cabin, the helmsman in the pilot house, or Murdoch Kutley in the engine room. You had to yell very loudly indeed to get Murdoch, and we usually just dropped marbles down the voice tube. There was a big bag of them tied to the top of the voice tube. Right next to the conning tower, which was open to the four winds and any of the seven seas that wanted to take the trouble to climb up, was a smokestack about six inches in diameter. The other end of the smokestack was connected with the fresh-water evaporators and *our* end was precisely at eye level. No matter which direction the wind came from, a rich odor of burning combs whipped across the conning tower. New officers, reporting aboard from cruisers or battleships, always blenched when they saw our conning tower, and we never qualified anyone for Officer of the Deck until he mastered the knack of shooting a mibby into the voice tube with sufficient force to get past the openings in the sea cabin and the pilot house. Even so, the conning tower afforded a magnificent view of the ship, and LST officers got sunburned earlier and stayed sunburned longer than officers in any other ship. They also got colder and wetter.

Sally drank all this in, and even made sketches. I was just explaining about the marbles when Lownes found us and reported that dinner was ready.

Dinner was wonderful. It was the nicest Christmas dinner I ever had in the Navy. Lownes had stuffed a lot of extra celery, including some with peanut butter, and had folded the napkins so they looked like full-dress cocked hats. He had even put candles on the table, and the wardroom phonograph was playing "Silent Night."

When he brought the turkey in, Sally took a drumstick. I reached for the other one, but Lownes hissed at me and when I looked around I saw Gruber in the doorway waiting for the turkey and shaking his head. He was holding one of the menus and pointing violently to the note at the bottom. I smiled, nodded my head, and settled for the neck and a wing.

After dinner Vlasser came in and reported that the movie would start in five minutes. I felt expansive.

"Vlasser," I said, "we have a guest. Suppose we let her pick the picture. Bring the books in."

"Sir?"

"Bring the books in." The crew had been promised the musical, but I was sure Sally would pick the right book and it seemed like a nice gesture.

Vlasser brought the books in, looking dubious. Sally flicked through the reviews. Suddenly her face brightened.

"I've always wanted to see this one," she said, pushing one of the books over.

Vlasser and I looked at it. It was *Gunga Din*.

"I think, maybe, the crew has already seen that one. Haven't they seen that one, Vlasser?"

"Yessir. Twicet. They *all* seen it."

"Perhaps we'd better pick another one. How about this?" I held up the musical.

"*I've* seen that one. It's no good. No good at all."

Vlasser looked desperate.

"Tell you what, miss. You let the crew see that musical. Afterward I go get *Gunga Din*, and we show it right here in the wardroom. Just for you, Miss. How's that?"

"Splendid, splendid!" I nodded vigorously. Vlasser grabbed the books and fled.

"Look," I said to Sally, "when do you have to leave?"

"I'm staying with some friends in Portsmouth," she said. "I'm driving down to Little Hominy tomorrow."

"Come back and see us tomorrow, before you go."

"Why?"

"Well, this is Christmas. Everybody's relaxing. Can't really see the ship when we aren't working."

"I *could* come, for a little while."

"Lunch? Yes? Please?"

"All right."

Then there was more chitchat about the Navy, but the conversation kept slipping off nautical subjects. By the time the musical was over I knew lots about Sally. She wasn't married. She had the measles when she was seven. She only used her Southern accent when she had the wrong change for bus drivers. She wasn't engaged, either.

Most of all, I knew I wanted to see her again.

I couldn't get her to stay for supper. I couldn't even get her to stay for *Gunga Din,* because her friends were expecting her back. She promised to come to lunch again (I kept checking this point) and I finally helped her on with her coat and saw her up to the quarterdeck. We said goodbye, and she picked her way across to the other ship and up to the rim of the dock. Then she turned and waved and I waved and a lot of men on both ships waved too.

It was quite the nicest Christmas I could remember.

CHAPTER 3

THE next morning the big shipyard whistle blew at eight o'clock; the liberty section scurried aboard; Murdoch and Rudolph, looking very well fed, squeaked in under the gun; three hundred workmen poured onto the ship; and the overhaul began.

Shipyard overhauls are periods of great crisis in the Navy. For eighteen months or so a ship putters along and the ship's force fixes whatever breaks down, with an occasional assist from a repair ship. After a year and a half, however, the accumulated list of machinery more or less permanently on the fritz starts to assume alarming proportions. Large parts wear out, gear breaks down that no one knows how to repair, and the only machinist in the Western Hemisphere capable of starting the LCVP motor on a cold morning gets transferred. In addition, the Engineering Officer has been collecting a scrapbook filled with what BuShips calls "Permanent Alterations," which may range from installing a new elevator in the tank deck to giving us a tripod mast. Other ships go through overhauls and get these alterations, and we begin to feel obsolescent.

Just when the Captain is convinced that his ship is in about the same condition the *Bonhomme Richard* was in after she tangled with the *Serapis*, and that the only thing keeping her afloat is the good clean moral life being led by the Engineering Officer, orders come to enter the shipyard. There is joy in the wardroom and there is joy in engineering spaces. Shipyards can do anything; the possibilities are limitless. The Captain has visions of a fully enclosed, air-conditioned conning tower, with a real leather armchair, and the sailors think of paint and perk up.

The subject of paint is a sensitive one. Paint, in fact, is a word that is charged with emotional impact. It ranks equally with "leave" and "Shore Patrol" and "midwatch," and is close on the heels of "Marilyn Monroe."

The difficulty is that ships are made of steel, and steel rusts, and the only way to stop rust is to cover the steel with paint. This sounds very simple indeed, and it is, but the catch is that something is always happening to paint. To begin with, it won't stay in place unless the metal it goes down on is absolutely sparkling. No old paint, no rust, no little grease spots. The slightest sign of these and the new paint curls right up and goes away. This means that whatever is to be painted has to be cleaned first, and this takes time. All over America clean-cut, patriotic boys are signing up for a career in the Navy, with enchanting visions of lean gray ships, abristle with guns, slicing through tropical seas. They have no difficulty envisioning themselves on the bridges of these ships, staring intently through binoculars at palm-fringed archipelagoes. Shortly after reporting to their first ships, however, these very same men are introduced to something called a chipping iron, a metal bar an inch wide and a foot long, with one tip bent over. It is the first piece of nautical gear they ever see, and they see a lot of it in the next few years.

Their very first day on the ship they look at the Plan of the Day, which will have the following entry on it:

> Training Program: Immediately after quarters all seamen will report to the Duty Boatswain's Mate for instruction and practical work in the removal of preservatives from metallic surfaces.

This is called on-the-job training and is a very modern concept.

Then they learn about chipping. By banging the chipping iron very hard on a metallic surface, a flake of pre-

servative about the size of an immature cockroach can be removed.

By industrious work an area almost a foot square can be bared in the course of a morning. Everybody works very industriously, because the instant you relax the noise stops, and the Duty Boatswain shows up at once to find out why. At this point the new sailor is convinced that he knows all there is to know about removing preservatives from metallic surfaces, and he is so right, but there is still quite a lot of paint to chip and he will chip for many a dreary day to come.

It never ends, because no matter how many men work how hard for how long, there is always more paint to chip off, and long, long before the entire ship is denuded the area they started in has aged and deteriorated and is ready for fresh attentions. Chipping irons never wear out, and they never break. Sailors may surreptitiously drop them overboard, but the boatswain invariably has new ones ready. No one has ever been able to make a boatswain admit that he has run out of chipping irons. Rudolph Rush claimed that eighteen and one half per cent of the United States defense budget was spent on chipping irons.

Putting paint down is almost as much trouble as getting it up. After the surface is clean it should immediately be covered with a coat of priming paint, which comes in many colors, usually orange. Priming is a wonderful rust inhibitant, but it in turn must be covered with gray paint because the priming, while death on rust, is delicate and wears off. Navy ships, therefore, frequently present a patchwork spectacle of old paint, bare metal, red, orange, yellow and green priming, and gray paint, and the efficiency of the ship's First Lieutenant can be judged miles away by the relative sizes of the different patches.

Even after the paint gets down, things happen to it. It gets walked on before it is dry, mostly, and it takes about two days to dry. First Lieutenants have been known to sit up all night with riot guns protecting freshly painted decks; they secure for breakfast and when they come out of the wardroom there are footprints all over the place. Even if it gets to dry, people will drag anchor chains over it, and, if everything fails, and the paint drys, they will go miles out of their way to find purple paint and spill it on the deck.

While Boatswain's Mates never run out of chipping irons, they do run out of paint. Paint is a fire hazard, and the amount that can be carried on a ship is strictly limited.

First Lieutenants have suffered breakdowns after chipping an entire superstructure down to bare metal and then discovering that there is no more paint, that the allowance has been overexpended and that none of the neighboring ships has as much as a teaspoonful to spare. This leads to what are known as "midnight requisitions."

A small ship must depend on midnight requisitions to keep herself in paint and powder. Big ships have so much money to spend that they have no trouble. Midnight requisitions are most apt to occur when small ships find themselves at docks near big ships, especially if the big ships are getting ready for long trips. All day long material arrives for the big ship, and her men work like beavers to get it aboard. If you have a really close friend in the supply depot, it is sometimes possible to arrange, say, for two hundred gallons of paint to be delivered just before quitting time in the afternoon. The big ship signs for this, and then, because there is a certain amount of muttering about liberty and union hours, her officers may decide to leave the stuff on the pier and get it aboard in the morning.

If those officers have any smart, however, they will get that stuff aboard if it takes all night, especially if they are berthed near small ships with lots of priming showing. At the very least they will put an armed guard on the pier. If the big ship omits these sensible precautions, activity on the small ships picks up. The Boatswain's Mates will linger near the quarterdeck. They will descend to the paint locker and estimate their needs. They will gaze long and reflectively at the lighting arrangements on the pier. They will confer with various seamen who have the duty that night, and exercise particular care in filling out the quarterdeck watch roster.

Shrieking Eagle was unsurpassed at planning these forays. Along about suppertime he would slip out on the pier and arrange one of the floodlights so that it shone full on the movie screen of the big ship. When the movie started there would be howls and whistles from the audience and the quarterdeck watch would look over the pier

to see if they could find someone in charge of the lights. Shrieking Eagle would wave at them and they would yell at him. He would nod understandingly and all at once *all* the lights on the pier would go out. When the picture was over, the lights would go on again, and hardly anybody would notice that the pile of five-gallon paint cans was now considerably smaller. No one would notice it, in fact, until the Supply Officer on the big ship got around to counting his cans, by which time the big ship was likely to be in Istanbul or Hong Kong or somewhere. The Supply Officer would make a lot of noise, but he spent most of his time counting paint cans anyway and hardly ever came out even, so no one would pay much attention to him.

The only major metal structure in the world that has the problem licked is the Golden Gate Bridge. It is covered with orange chromate priming and *only* orange chromate priming, which is why it is called the Golden Gate.

Machines do exist which remove paint, ranging from pneumatic chipping hammers through sandblasters to homemade devices called "jitterbugs," which not only remove all paint but a thin layer of steel as well, not to mention fingers and toes. Most of these devices work on compressed air, except the jitterbug, which is electrical and chips beautifully until it is run through a puddle of water on a deck. Then there are sparks and howls and much smoke and all the lights on the ship go out and the hapless paint remover is carried away and put to peeling potatoes for a day or two until his nervous system is functioning again.

All these machines are legendary on LSTs because they are expensive, and LSTs don't have much money. Shipyards have lots of money, though, and great numbers of pneumatic chipping hammers and sandblasters and jitterbugs, and the most junior Seaman Apprentice, banging away in the bilges with his chipping iron, has visions of hordes of well-equipped shipyard employees coming to his rescue. Everybody, in fact, has visions except the shipyard officials. They have no illusions whatsoever. They have a given amount of money and a set amount of time, and they draw a very sharp line between what really has to be done and what the ship thinks it would be nice to have done.

Just before the ship gets to the yard, the Captain and the Engineering Officer collect all their lists and complaints and requests and go to the shipyard and have a long conference with the yard officials. During the course of this conference, from which the Engineering Officer will emerge twitching, the yard officials will use the phrase "budgetary limitations" no less than seventy-four times, and the Captain will begin every third sentence with "but." The shipyard people will go over the lists and cross off items like "Install new bunk in sea cabin. Present bunk fourteen inches shorter than present Captain," and "Devise, manufacture and install shoeshine machine in crew's quarters." Eventually a list will be hammered out, with the

Engineering Officer fighting a losing battle over pet items, all of which he will file away and drag out again in another eighteen months. Some of the choicer items have been passed down from Engineering Officer to Engineering Officer since shortly after Manila Bay.

When the overhaul actually starts, the ship and its organization are rapidly reduced to utter chaos. Much of the machinery to be overhauled is delicate, and the shipyard does not like to attempt repairs aboard. People go around hanging tags on equipment reading "Ship to Shore," and all of this equipment is ripped out and dragged off somewhere in the yard to be worked on. Some of the machinery so marked is big and holes have to be cut in decks and bulkheads to get it out. Within three days the Captain stops thinking in terms of the *Bonhomme Richard* and starts thinking in terms of the *Maine*.

Since all of the ship's machinery is out of action, water, steam and electricity have to be piped aboard in cables and hoses. In no time at all the ship looks like a caterpillar getting ready for a hard winter. Lines snake all over the ship, coming from BuYards and Docks knows where and going BuShips knows where. Some gurgle and some hiss and others just throb quietly. Turning on a faucet is an adventure, with about equal chances for silence, compressed air, steam, or hydraulic fluid. The noise level rises and rises, lights go off without warning, and desks are removed from under typewriters you are using. The galley range disappears with noon chow for one hundred men in it, and the radio gang is marooned in the radio shack when a ladder is taken out to have new treads installed.

The personnel situation also goes.to pot. Every ship has a Watch, Quarter and Station Bill which has been put together with infinite care and on which every man aboard has been assigned a job for every situation. We could, for example, beach the ship, put a landing force ashore, retract from the beach, rig for heavy weather, send off a rescue party to another ship, and then stand by to receive survivors, all in quick succession with no visible confusion. The instant a ship gets into a yard, however, the leakage starts. Part of the crew immediately decamps on leave, having been waiting for this opportunity for some time. A good number of the rest have to be sent off to various schools, which will keep them anywhere from one day to six months. In the meantime, the Executive Officer is left with one third the normal complement and a demand for labor that has tripled and is steadily going up. What he particularly requires is an unlimited supply of Warm Bodies.

A Warm Body is a man with at least one arm and two fingers who can pick something up when he is told to. Warm Bodies can carry boxes, count small objects, turn on lights, chip paint, and sweep. Normally they are of relatively little value to a ship. In a shipyard they come into their own.

Warm Body material can be found almost everywhere. Lester Wallace may be the finest radar operator in the

Atlantic Fleet, and the final product of two years' technical training, but if the radar set has been taken away, Lester Wallace is a Warm Body, and will remain one until the radar set comes back.

No one has ever figured out how to weld on one side of a steel bulkhead without getting the other side hot, so each shipyard welder (and they are legion) has to have a man stationed in the adjoining compartment to see that nothing catches fire. If the welder is working in a corner, he may need as many as six of these fire watchers to cover all the compartments that are getting hotted up. Fire watchers do not need any skill beyond the ability to distinguish between an object that is on fire and one that is not, and it is a job almost all Warm Bodies can perform with distinction.

The Executive Officer is normally a person who may have to sign up to three thousand pieces of paper a month, some of which are important. In the shipyard, however, only one piece of paper really registers with him—the scrawled list of Warm Bodies he keeps in his notebook and doles out as the occasion demands. People are forever popping up and saying, "Gotta paint the mast before they rewire the range light. They're waiting now. Gimme four names." The Executive Officer then takes out his little notebook and produces four names, haggling fiercely over whether or not four men can get on the mast ladder at the same time. The Master at Arms appears and says, "Three mess cooks is on leave and you sent Hinkle to that telephone-talking school. Gimme three names." If the Executive Officer gives the Master at Arms only two names instead of three, chow will be an hour late and will continue to be late until the third Warm Body is produced. Then the shipyard supervisor appears and states that while he is committed to reboring the cylinders in the LCVP engine, nothing was said about getting the engine over to the other side of the shipyard where the right machine shop is, and can he please have six names.

After a while, all the names are gone and the Executive Officer is reduced to body-snatching, grabbing Warm Bodies from one job before it is finished in order to get other jobs started. He experiments. Can a Warm Body slice turnips and fire-watch at the same time? The answer is always no. Executive Officers have been known to prowl the ship during overhauls, grabbing everybody who didn't have something heavy in both hands at the time and putting him to work elsewhere. In extreme cases they go to pieces and tell the yeoman to cancel all leaves and get everybody back to the ship at once. These Executive Officers lie in their bunks at night and curse whoever put the kibosh on the idea of the press gang, which strikes them as the sanest and soundest of systems.

Toward the end of the overhaul a dim hint of daylight appears on the horizon. The machinery starts to return and is bolted and welded into place. The leave parties return, raring to go. The school contingents are aboard again, filled with strange skills. The Executive Officer finds there are actually four men aboard with nothing to do. The Captain and the shipyard supervisor start exchanging complimentary letters, replete with phrases like "Due to the magnificent nature of the co-operation extended by your men . . ." and "Although faced with technical and administrative problems of an almost insurmountable order, you nevertheless managed to . . ."

At last the ship, refurbished and sparkling, steams slowly out of the yard, with one or two workmen tucked into corners and trying frantically to finish a last minor job or two, and one overlooked compressed-air hose thrashing around in the engine room. All the names are back on the Watch, Quarter and Station Bill; the Executive Officer, when his voice returns, will be able to pass out scores of names; and all the Warm Bodies have been taken in hand and will eventually be turned into finished man-o'-war's men. The overhaul is finished, and everybody has a year and a half to recuperate in before the ordeal must be faced again.

By nine o'clock the process was in full swing. The shipyard had cut a hole in the main deck and was already engaged in pulling the evaporators out. The evaporator boiler came out too, and Murdoch shortly reported in triumph that we *had* been smelling combs burning; a box of them had slipped behind the boiler while being transferred from the ship's storeroom.

I spent a half hour in the ship's office, going over my final, irrevocable list of names and watching the yeoman defend his last desk, practically with his life. My list dwindled even as I went over it. Rudolph showed up and asked for six names to carry all the navigational equipment off to be adjusted. I gave him two. Somebody from the shipyard wanted five names to move the galley equipment to an unused building, because our galley was uninhabitable. I figured this was important and I let him have the names. This reduced me to three names and Shrieking Eagle. Three of these names went for fire watchers, and when I tried to get out of the office to rustle up some reserves I found I was trapped by a solid bank of air hoses strung past the door. The yeoman and I clawed a small opening in the maze and yelled for help, but someone was riveting in the passageway and we couldn't even hear each other.

In about an hour the Quarterdeck Watch fought his way in to the door to tell me I had a visitor topside. He finally had to write it out on a pad the yeoman gave him, and we passed him a note to go find the superintendent and get us out.

The superintendent finally showed up with a worker, and the riveting stopped and all the lines were uncoiled and we stepped out.

"I *asked* if anyone was in there," the worker said glumly as he restrung the lines.

Sally was waiting on the edge of the dock, writing notes and asking questions.

"Good morning!" she said when I had climbed up to the

rim of the dock. "I'm getting a terrific story. What's that for?"

She pointed to one of the lines leading over the edge of the dock and down to the ship. I looked at it closely.

"Compressed air for the chipping manifold. How are you?"

"Fine," Sally said, writing it down.

A workman came up, disconnected the end of the line, and jumped to one side as a fine spray of Diesel oil rose in the air. Sally looked at it, and then erased something in her notebook.

Chief Boatswain Popper came up to us. "Higgins sprained his thumb. Gimme a name."

"Shrieking Eagle," I said, crossing off the last one on my list. "Sally, we can't eat on the ship. How about lunch in town?"

"Fine. I've got my car here. Is it like this every day?"

"In the yard, it is."

Murdoch came up the gangway.

"Hey, they started to cut the stern winch loose. I need fire watchers. Gimme five names."

"Sure," I said. "Merrill, Lynch, Pierce, Fenner and Beane. You got the watch, kid. I'll be back in an hour."

As we reached Sally's car the shipyard whistle blew and the racket gradually died down for lunch. We drove along the edge of the dock, and I could see Murdoch on the quarterdeck at the P.A. system.

"Now hear this. Merrill, Lynch, Pierce, Fenner and

Beane, lay up to the quarterdeck. Merrill, Lynch . . ."

We went to a restaurant in Portsmouth and we had lunch. We didn't talk about the Navy, or about newspapers, and I've never been able to remember exactly what we did talk about, because by the time the coffee arrived I was in love. This didn't make any sense to me at all, but there it was.

"You look sort of green," Sally said, stirring her coffee. "Was the lunch all right?"

"Green? The lunch was fine. I'm in love."

"With me?"

"Yes. Does this happen very often? I mean, if it does, just say so, and maybe it'll go away."

"No-o. I mean, it doesn't happen *very* often. It did once, though."

"Oh?"

"Well, he never did say anything, and finally he went away."

"Will you marry me?"

"He might come back."

"How long ago was this?"

"Year ago. Two."

"He won't show. Will you marry me?"

"You're sure? About being in love?"

"Reasonably. I don't know. I never was before."

"You do look a little funny."

"That's what I mean."

We looked at each other and I poured some coffee on the tablecloth.

Sally finally cleared her throat. "Look, how long are you all going to be in this yard?"

"Three weeks."

"Right now I have to go home to Little Hominy. The day after New Year's I go back to New York. You might come see me one place or the other and we could talk it over some more."

"What's the matter with this afternoon?"

"I have to get to Little Hominy. Besides, I need some time to think about it."

"I can't leave the ship on leave till the skipper gets back."

"Well, you write me when you can, if you still think it's a good idea. Hominy's closer, but you can get to New York quicker."

We left the restaurant, and I had to go back to pay the bill. When I came out she was in her car. We said goodbye and she drove off, and I started to walk back to the shipyard.

It still didn't make any sense to me, but there it was. I was distinctly in love. I was quite sure of that. I might even be engaged, for all I knew. I had certainly proposed, and while I couldn't remember being accepted, I was absolutely certain I hadn't been turned down.

I got back to the yard and the whistle was blowing to start work again. At the edge of the drydock I stopped and looked down at the ship. It looked different. More like an office than it used to, if you know what I mean. They were going to paint the wardroom when the overhaul was over, and Schuyler and I had had quite an argument about what color to use, and, standing there, I suddenly realized I really didn't give a damn what color they painted it.

I could see Murdoch. He was still on the quarterdeck. He had three sailors standing next to him and was holding one firmly by the elbow. A faint voice drifted up from the P.A. system.

"Now hear this. Fenner and Beane, bear a hand and lay up to the quarterdeck on the double."

CHAPTER 4

THE overhaul proceeded briskly. From a nadir, at which practically nothing movable was left aboard the ship, and what remained looked more like a shoebox than ever, we gradually attained a zenith, with all the new gear installed and a brave coat of paint taking a few years off our age. The Captain called twice from Montana, was reassured both times that all was progressing smoothly, and sent us a postcard with a picture of a trout stream where he had almost caught a fish.

Everything proceeded so smoothly, in fact, that the

shipyard broke down and took care of two of our pet projects. They still wouldn't touch the Captain's bunk or the soft-drink machine, but they did put a metal screen around the conning tower, chin-high, and they put a new voice tube in down to the engine room. One of the foremen had skidded on a marble and sprained his ankle.

I wrote to Sally every day, and after a while she started answering me. She warned me never to try to telephone to Little Hominy, or Big Hominy, for that matter, unless it was an emergency; she would explain about this when she saw me. Little Hominy was only 208 miles from Norfolk, but it was a little hard to reach by car unless someone who had been there before first showed you the way. I didn't have a car, but Sally said the Atlantic, Piedmont, and Beauregard Railroad had a depot in Big Hominy. She never traveled the AP & B herself, so she couldn't tell me about schedules. The important thing to remember was that unless you got off in Lye, Virginia, and went across the tracks to where the fireman and engineer ate and had your lunch with them, you didn't get any lunch.

She sent all sorts of other news. The editor liked her story. He didn't print it, because he said it wasn't objective, but he was promoting her to teen-age fiction. She had also heard from the man she thought had been in love with her, and he had been in love, all right, and had married the girl and she had just had twins. I answered that I was enormously happy for him, and that as far as I could see nothing now stood in our way.

I told Murdoch and Rudolph and Schuyler I was in love, and they didn't believe me. Schuyler said things like that just didn't happen on Navy ships. He himself got engaged two or three times a year, and he was inclined to treat the subject lightly. Murdoch and Rudolph finally began to take me seriously, after they saw how easily I gave up about the wardroom paint, and I was treated to a number of lectures on housing, in-laws, and the baby-sitter futures market.

The Captain finally came back, looking wonderfully refreshed, and we finished our overhaul. We shifted to the piers at Little Creek and were told to stay there two weeks or so for refresher training. This all sounded very nice and I put in for a weekend leave to visit Sally in New York.

She sounded pleased when I called her Wednesday night from Norfolk.

"I keep forgetting what you look like. The society editor says this doesn't necessarily mean anything, one way or the other."

"I remember exactly what *you* look like."

"The society editor said you would. She said that doesn't necessarily mean anything, one way or the other, either."

"It does to me. Will you marry me?"

"You call me when you get in Friday. We'll talk about it then."

All the way back to Little Creek from town I thought about Friday. It would be a wonderful weekend. We could announce our engagement Saturday, or maybe Sunday if the train was late. Captain O'Gara hadn't even heard about Sally, we had been so busy shifting berths since he got back, and this seemed like a good moment to tell him. He and Murdoch were sitting in the wardroom when I got back, and I was so busy thinking about how to begin that Murdoch's being aboard at that time of night didn't register.

"Her name is Sally," I began.

"We're going to Puerto Rico," the Captain answered.

"She has red hair."

"In six hours."

"I think I'm engaged."

"Four hundred Marines are coming aboard at five o'clock."

"It was the funniest thing how it all started."

Captain O'Gara reached over and shook me gently.

All the good news was unloaded in one ice-cold bucketful. The LST originally slated for Puerto Rico had broken a propeller blade and couldn't sail. We were to go instead. The Marines were already on their way. The ship's store was out of cigarettes and there was bad weather off Hatteras. Shrieking Eagle was ashore, and had last been seen at a revival meeting. The last news could have been considerably worse; if Shrieking Eagle got converted again, he could be counted on to stay aboard for a month or so. With the ship headed for the Caribbean this was important. It was backbreaking work translating from Chickasaw to English to Spanish.

I skinned back up the pier and called Sally again. She sounded sleepy. I explained that these things happened in the Navy and that I would get leave the instant I got back. She told me to at least send her my picture. I told her the only one I had was taken in a Neapolitan Five-and-Ten Cent Store, and that I had been wearing a red beard at the time. The thought suddenly struck me that all our children would have red hair, but I didn't say anything over the phone. I asked her to marry me again just as the operator signaled that time was up.

"Well, I promise not to marry anybody else before you get back."

It was the best I could do. Navy men have sailed off into the night with a lot less.

At five in the morning, promptly, the Marines arrived. They marched up the gangway in single file, and were mustered by the grandfather of all master sergeants, who stood at the top of the gangway inquiring "Ick? Ack? Uck? Awk?" and was answered "Hunh!" by each Marine in turn. The very last Marine answered "How!" and turned out to be Shrieking Eagle. He was wearing Marine boots, a helmet, a poncho, and nothing else. We got the Marine major to muster his people again, because we had the feeling one might be missing. He said nonsense, and insisted none of his men could get lost while they were what he called "in convoy," but he didn't know Shrieking Eagle. Just before we sailed he discovered that a Corporal Gowanus was not aboard. He was thunderstruck and implied that Gowanus must have fallen overboard in the dark, and he wanted to lower the boats and start a search, but just as the gangway was coming up a Shore Patrol jeep arrived with Gowanus. He was wearing a handsome handwoven blanket, and he had a bump on his forehead and couldn't remember where the blanket came from.

After the Marines were all aboard their vehicles arrived. Nobody ever understands why the Marine Corps carries so many vehicles around with them. I have even seen Marines puzzled by it. Tanks were fine; everybody knows that the Marines use tanks, and we could even go along with trucks and jeeps and ambulances. The Marines, however, always have a load of peculiar mechanical marvels. Bulldozers, road graders, steam shovels and steam rollers banged and rattled aboard and were stowed on the tank deck by Schuyler. As First Lieutenant, he was responsible for getting them all lashed down, so they wouldn't slide in a seaway. Tanks were heavy enough to stay put, but the other items presented problems. Schuyler bore a particular animosity to something called a sheep's foot tamper, which he swore had been specifically designed to remove metal fittings from LST decks and which had nothing by which you could tie it down.

By six in the morning we were off. The Captain bought a copy of the Norfolk *Ledger-Dispatch* to check the tides against the quartermaster's calculations, and we dropped our pilot outside Little Creek and swung into Thimble

Shoals Channel. We rounded the Cape, turned south, and rang up full speed ahead.

An LST has five forward speeds: ahead one third, ahead two thirds, ahead standard, ahead full, and something dramatically known as "flank." All of them are roughly the equivalent of eight knots, depending on the wind. Flank is a little faster, maybe nine or ten knots, but things rattle a lot and the Engineering Officer comes up to the bridge every now and again looking worried but without saying anything. With a head wind, the Operations Officer gets worried at flank speed too, because little bits of electronic gear begin to fall off the mast and it takes a long time to identify some of them. One night off Haiti a large electric switch came down and almost brained Schuyler, who had the watch. It took us two weeks to identify it, and we were all stumped until Lownes saw it and told us it was part of the vacuum cleaner.

We reached Hatteras at sundown. Some day a ship will arrive off Hatteras and it will be broad daylight and a gentle breeze will be blowing. Shortly thereafter the final trumpet will undoubtedly sound. Until then, ships will continue to round Hatteras in pitch-blackness and with a Force Six wind, and Captains will continue to wonder why the hell they didn't put in for the Pacific Fleet when they had the chance.

Captain O'Gara slowed to ahead two thirds, with no appreciable effect on the ship's motion, and all hands braced for a rough night. An LST is equipped with what in naval architectural circles are referred to as "bluff bows." To all landlubbers and most sailors who have served in them they look flat as a pancake. LSTs also have flat bottoms and no keels. This is supposed to facilitate beaching, and it may be all very well on a beach, but even LSTs can't spend all their time on beaches and when they retract they pay through the nose. To make up for the lack of a keel they have been given twin screws, but about all this accomplishes is to double the chances of fouling the stern cable when you are attempting to retract. Shiphandling, in most ships, is a fine art. In LSTs the trick is to find out, by gentle elicitation, what the ship really wants to do and then try to help her. Other ships slice through the waves. An LST can only clobber them over their little pointed heads and hope they go away before the bow doors cave in.

When a loaded LST traveling south at a majestic eight knots collides with a wave headed north at five knots, the results below decks are impressive. The ship stops abruptly, except for the vehicles on the tank deck, which try to keep going. The ship then tries to avoid the argument by going sideways, and picks up forward speed in a series of thunderous jolts, each one of which is hotly disputed by the water up forward. Since the ship is limber (this is another nautical term and refers to a quality usually encountered in fly rods), the bows may be rolling to port while the stern is still rolling to starboard. Viewed from either end of the tank deck, the effect is roughly similar to looking up a subway aisle as the train rounds a curve.

The crew was used to all this. We had our seasick sailors, but nobody paid any attention to them. The ship's tone had been set by Captain O'Gara the very first week he was aboard. Rudolph was also new and was slated for the midwatch. At a quarter to twelve he sent word to the bridge that he was too ill to stand his watch, and the messenger added that he personally was convinced of Rudolph's sincerity. O'Gara nodded calmly and said, "Quartermaster, take three men, go below, and bring up Mr. Rush." Rudolph stood, if I may be permitted the expression, his watch.

What our passengers made of all the commotion was only too evident. At the first large wave, a procession of anxious faces appeared in the hatches and a general interest was evinced in the small-boat situation.

The next wave thundered aboard, rolled aft through the vehicles lashed on the main deck (flushing out a few defenders of the thesis that it is better in the open) and soaked all the faces in the hatches. All of these faces promptly disappeared, to be replaced by new faces, looking progressively more and more unhappy. I even caught a glimpse of Corporal Gowanus, still wearing his blanket. He now had *two* bumps on his forehead.

Schuyler was ranging through the tank deck with a working party, doubling the lashings whenever it looked as if a vehicle wanted to travel on without us, and even up on the conning tower, above the wind, we could hear his admonitions to the sheep's foot tamper. In a short lull Schuyler came up to the bridge and reported that a number of Marines had taken their posts in their tanks and jeeps and bulldozers. The two ambulances were especially popular.

At four in the morning the weather was moderating a little, and we got a report that the soft-drink machine was out of order again. At first we decided to let this go until morning, but Chief Popper reported that almost every Marine on the ship was lined up and waiting; they hadn't eaten any supper, and they were so dehydrated that if they didn't get any soda pop, he was afraid they weren't going to last until morning.

The soft-drink machine was tricky. About a month after it was installed, a check valve failed and backed carbonated water into all the drinking fountains. After that it exploded, once, and then settled down to not dropping the cup into place and spraying its ingredients all over whoever wanted to get a drink. If you got your own cup first it cunningly overshot and doused your shoes with syrup. It also had undependable notions about change-making, but since it paid off in occasional bursts of nickels about as often as it withheld the correct change, everybody accepted it as a sporting gamble. The best way to handle it was to use a thin dime, kick it hard as it started to whirr, and then jump to the *left*.

Whenever it broke down completely, Shrieking Eagle had to be sent for. He did something to it with an ice pick, after which it would operate, after a fashion. We sent for him now, and soon the characteristic whirr and the howls of the Marines at the head of the line rose faintly above the subsiding noises of the storm.

By five o'clock Hatteras was safely astern and Captain O'Gara retired to his sea cabin. The Marines settled down to fitful slumber, and the ship lumbered on through the darkness. Captain O'Gara also slept fitfully. Very few Captains at sea sleep otherwise. They suffer from an occupational *Angst* that sooner or later something catastrophic is bound to happen and that when it does the Officer of the Deck will not call them in time.

Bosworth O'Gara, for example, had taken all the usual precautions. The sea cabin was handy to the bridge—directly below it, in fact—and O'Gara always left the door propped open. He slept fully clothed, with his ear jammed as closely to the voice tube as he could get it, ignoring the icy salt water that every now and again sloshed down the tube and down the back of his neck. One foot always dangled over the edge of the bunk, partially because the bunk was too short and partially to allow him a running start if he did get called. On the conning tower was his Night Order Book, with the night's entries initialed daily by every watch-stander. This listed all the navigational lights and course changes that were to be expected, with explicit instructions about how soon to call him if the lights didn't show up, and when he wanted to be called in the morning. The standing orders were at the front of the book, in red ink, and finished with "Do not ever hesitate to call me. I am to be called for all contacts. I will never be angry if you call me at night. I promise, now. Please."

When I reported to my first ship I was filled with a newly commissioned officer's fear of collisions. The very last lecture I had ever received at the Naval Academy had

been delivered by a rear admiral who had written a book on the Rules of the Nautical Road. He started his talk to the graduating class with "Gentlemen, it has rarely been my good fortune to address so large an audience of potential colliders. Statistics prove that three out of five of you will be involved in collisions in the next two decades."

He finished by reminding us that if it were our last conscious act as Officer of the Deck, to be sure and call the skipper.

Almost all skippers get called before the situation approaches what is quaintly known as "in extremis," but it was a long time before I learned just what is really worth waking a skipper up for. My first underway night watch was stood under the tutelage of Lieutenant Parrish, who could and frequently did tell new officers that he had wrung more salt water out of his jock strap than they had sailed over. Around one in the morning, fifty miles off Cape Henry, I saw a light. It was a trawler, about six miles abaft the beam, and dropping astern. To a new ensign, a light is a light, however. I informed Parrish, who commended me for my diligence.

"I'll tell the Captain," I added.

"Hell, don't wake the poor bastard up," Parrish said.

I was flabbergasted. This was how collisions occurred. This violated every tenet of the naval profession. My feelings showed in my face.

"You might as well learn right now, kid," Parrish said, and walked over to the voice tube. He banged it with his parallel rulers and shouted into it.

"Cap'n! Cap'n! Wake up!"

Out of the tube came a sleep-drugged voice. "Uh! Uh? Wazza mat'?"

Parrish smiled sweetly. "Piss call, you old son of a bitch!"

I braced myself for the explosion. There was a moment's pause.

"Ver' well. Call me if it gets any closer."

CHAPTER

THE island of Vieques, to the east of Puerto Rico, is home to about seven Puerto Ricans, five horses and a goat. The Puerto Ricans evidently like it, the horses are philosophical, and no one has ever asked the goat how he felt. The center of the southern coast is graced by an abandoned coconut plantation known as Gonzales' Folly. Every so often the Navy descends in great force on the island, scaring hell out of the goat and giving the ships and the Marine Corps an opportunity to try out their latest amphibious techniques.

Our particular group of Marines was an advance party

sent down to ready the camp sites for the coming invasion, so once they were ashore we had the little bay to ourselves.

We had beached early in the morning, landed our men and equipment, retracted, and were now swinging at anchor a mile or so off shore. Beachings took a lot out of everybody. Everything had to be just right—tide, wind, beach slope, sea condition, ballast, stern anchor winch, and Bosworth O'Gara's digestion. Since the Captain had only a limited measure of control over at least half of these factors, and absolutely none over the others, beachings could be sticky. The general idea was to run up to the beach, dropping the stern anchor while still a bit off shore, and then to get stuck on the beach hard enough to stay there during tide shifts but not so hard as to make the beach a permanent home. Getting up on the beach was not very hard, except for dropping the anchor at the right instant. Dropping it too soon and running out all the cable was almost as bad as not dropping it at all, in which case it had to be slung between two small boats, taken out, and dropped by hand. This was an operation that most seamanship texts devoted an entire chapter to and that only Shrieking Eagle faced with equanimity.

The big trick was getting *off* the beach. Going astern on the engines just piled sand under the hull; going ahead got some of the sand out but lost sight of the primary objective, which was to move seaward and not inland. The best system was to "fishtail," using the rudder and the engines going in opposite directions and keeping a constant strain on the stern cable. The cable wasn't strong enough to use in pulling the ship off; its sole function was to keep the fantail pointed seaward during the few agonizing moments when the ship was floating freely but as yet had no stern-way on. Without the strain on the stern cable, the ship was in danger of swinging parallel to the beach, too close in to turn. This condition was known as "broaching" and was a dirty word in nautical circles.

We had never broached, and we had always got off the beach without having to send for a tug, although once we had to get the Marines to give us a shove with a bulldozer. Now that we were retracted, we were going to anchor for the day, enjoy the sunshine and hold holiday routine.

On our ship, holiday routine at anchor meant fishing. The instant the sea detail secured, fishing lines went out fore and aft, and once in a great while a fish would be caught. If the catch was of a respectable size, the happy angler would receive congratulations, trot all over the ship looking for someone to photograph him with his catch, and then disappear into the galley to make private arrangements with Gruber, who operated on a fifty-fifty basis and was highly regarded as an ichthyologist. In tropical waters, a large percentage of the fish are either tasteless or down-right poisonous, and Gruber was the final authority. Since he did not particularly care for fish, he turned thumbs down on a large percentage of the items brought to the galley for his inspection. He never fished himself.

In this, as in other matters, Shrieking Eagle was the thorn

in the side of the ship and also of the Captain. For Shrieking Eagle could fish. From any body of water larger than a Mason jar he could extract fish. Whenever we anchored, Shrieking Eagle would drop whatever he was doing, go to the rail, peer overboard and frown reflectively. Then he would proceed to the recreation locker, pick out a hook, twenty yards of the first line he could lay his hands on, and a float. The hook he baited with bubble gum, a twist of paper from a cigarette package, or a bit of red yarn. This he threw overboard, tying the end to the railing, and went about his business. When mess call sounded he hauled up the line, took whatever fish was on the hook (and there was invariably a fish on the hook) to Gruber, and waited until Gruber dressed and cooked it. Gruber always cooked Shrieking Eagle's fishes and they were delicious. Then Shrieking Eagle, picking his teeth, would stroll back to the fantail, where Captain O'Gara could usually be found examining Shrieking Eagle's hook and line and grinding his teeth.

What made all this so distressing was that Bosworth O'Gara was also a born fisherman. That is, he fished. Incessantly. But when he lay in his cradle and all the good fairies perched on the rim with their gifts, making him a good shiphandler and an excellent acey-deucy man, there came one with a miniature rod who waved it thrice and said, "Thou shalt not catch fish," and Bosworth O'Gara never did. Not ever. It was not for lack of trying.

The ship's Welfare Fund, with ever the least little prodding from the bridge, had provided us with a magnificent collection of fishing tackle. Other ships might go in for fancy baseball uniforms with the name of the ship emblazoned on the back. Not us. We had aqualungs. We were prepared to cope with everything from *betta splendens*, the Siamese fighting fish, to adolescent sperm whales. And wherever we went, Bosworth O'Gara checked out his gear and set forth full of hope.

In Norway, he went up a fjord to a Royal Preserve under the guidance of a Norwegian rear admiral. The admiral caught seven salmon, one four ounces shy of the world's record.

The Captain got a nice sunburn.

In Scotland, he was taken to a trout stream by a man whose family had owned it for seven hundred years. The stretch he fished had been mentioned favorably by Izaak Walton. Bosworth O'Gara spent nine hours there, only quitting in total darkness. His host caught seventeen trout and read the first nine chapters of *Riders of the Purple Sage*.

The Captain got hay fever.

In Greenland, an Eskimo took him out in a kayak, harpooned a walrus, and caught eleven unidentified fish.

The Captain was bitten by a small male seal when he inadvertently dabbled his fingers in the water.

Bosworth O'Gara's worst day had been off Palermo, when he organized a skin-diving expedition. The aqualungs had just arrived and had not been tried out. O'Gara collected Rudolph and Murdoch and set out in the LCVP, with Shrieking Eagle as coxswain. In a cove highly recommended by the indigenous professionals, Shrieking Eagle cut the motor and watched each officer hoist himself to the gunwale and plop overboard. In addition to his aqualung, each officer was equipped with rubber fins, a spring spear, and a knife. Murdoch had a large net he invented, which you were supposed to tow.

The waters were absolutely teeming with marine life. No sooner had the party submerged than Rudolph surfaced in pursuit of a large bonito. He had lost his spear and was stabbing at the bonito with his knife. Then Murdoch encountered a small octopus, on which he tried out his net, but it developed that the octopus could swim faster than Murdoch could. The octopus retired with full honors, and Murdoch discarded the net.

From then on, for an hour or so, the hunting was good. Rudolph had recovered his spear, and he and Murdoch each landed a number of fish. Shrieking Eagle sat in the stern sheets, sunning himself and munching sandwiches, and spotting fresh game.

Late in the afternoon a four-foot shark appeared,

and Bosworth O'Gara, still fishless, went after him.

The Captain was determined to get him and the shark, obviously puzzled by the large apparition thrashing toward him and thrusting ahead with his spear, backed cautiously off. Murdoch and Rudolph also backed off, sharks being sharks, and the Captain and his prey slowly circled in the agitated waters. The shark in his retreat finally cornered Rudolph between his tail and the hull of the LCVP. Rudolph, mustering up his courage, lunged at the shark's tail just as the Captain, seeing the shark pause, launched his final attack. The shark, jabbed at fore and aft, took off for the Straits of Messina, and the Captain, dimly aware of a large white form in the swirling foam, thrust home. Rudolph shot straight up out of the water with the Captain's fish spear firmly planted in his thigh, and O'Gara surfaced, clawing at his goggles and howling "I got him! I got a fish! I got a fish!"

It took Murdoch a good five minutes to convince the Captain that the shark had gotten away. The Captain had little sympathy for Rudolph, and was under the impression that Rudolph had somehow shot himself. When he finally realized that it was *his* spear that Rudolph had just extracted from his leg, he took it as a personal affront, railed bitterly at Rudolph for "flushing *his* shark" and called on heaven, earth and Murdoch Kutley to witness that it was by the merest mishap that he had not, finally, caught a fish.

The trip back to the LST was not sweetened by Shrieking Eagle. Rudolph, nursing his injury, had lost his ID tags in the excitement, and Shrieking Eagle went overboard to find them. He not only got the ID cards; when he surfaced he had a large flounder in his left hand.

The Captain refused to have anything more to do with aqualungs, claiming they were "unsportsmanlike," an opinion fully shared by Rudolph.

Off Vieques, when Mess Call sounded, Shrieking Eagle again had a fish. It was a monster, five feet long, with great scaly gill covers and pediculated fins. Shrieking Eagle took it to the galley, but for once Gruber refused to cook a catch of his, claiming that the object involved was no true fish but a cross between a barracuda and an alligator. Shrieking Eagle was highly incensed, sought out Vlasser and had himself photographed, and retired to the fantail. Here he sliced up his catch, doused it with ketchup, and downed it raw with apparent relish.

At sunset we set the Special Sea Detail and prepared to get underway. Earlier, an LCVP had been sent in with a small liberty party and the Mail Orderly, who was to hike over to the Marine airstrip to get our mail. As the ship gathered way, the LCVP moved in under the davit heads, hooked on, and was hauled up. It was only when the LCVP had been secured and the beach was a good three miles behind us that we discovered there was a goat aboard. Some of the men in the LCVP had wandered inland to buy a few fresh coconuts. None of the Puerto Ricans could change the ten-dollar bill which was all they had with them, so they had to take the goat in change.

O'Gara's first reaction was to pitch the beast overboard and let him swim for it; there was still enough daylight for even a goat to see the beach. The goat, however, wasn't having any; this was his one chance to get the hell off Vieques, and he intended to make the most of it. A small working party managed to corner him on the main deck forward, but anyone attempting to get forward of Frame Six risked a stellar role in the Moment of Truth.

He acted, in fact, so much like a bull that he was named El Toro. We finally drove him onto the elevator with hoses, lowered him to the tank deck, and turned him loose. He promptly made himself at home and by the time we got back to Norfolk he was on friendly, if guarded, terms with most of the crew.

It was a glorious sunset. The sea was calm, we were headed home, and before us lay two weeks of what was marked on the Operations Schedule as "Lv & Upkp." There were steak and pumpkin pie for dinner, a good movie scheduled, and the mail was being sorted below. The interlude was perfect, one of those brief, lovely evenings that are responsible for so many re-enlistments.

Lightning didn't strike until the midwatch. Vlasser woke me at two in the morning and thrust the radio message board under my nose. I told him to call me if it got any closer. He shook me again, and I inspected the message by the light of his flashlight.

IN VIEW YOUR PERFORMANCE LAST INSPECTION AM SCHEDULING ADDITIONAL ADMINISTRATIVE INSPECTION TWO WEEKS FOLLOWING YOUR RETURN X EXPECT RADICAL IMPROVEMENTS X BINTLE

Naval officers rapidly become accustomed to waking up instantly and grasping the essentials of complicated situations.

"Who?" I asked.

"Yes, sir," Vlasser replied.

"Bintle?"

"Yes, sir."

"Here?"

"Yes, sir."

"Oh my God."

"Yes, sir."

There have been names in military history calculated to strike dismay into their own forces. "*Attention, le Maréchal Martinet arrive!*", "*Achtung, Friedrich kommt!*" and "*Onone! Yamashita-san mairimasu!*" have all been cries certain to raise at least a small flurry of activity in the units in which they have been voiced. The impact, however, was negligible compared to the emotions evoked by the name of Oliver Bintle.

Commander Oliver Bintle had one function in life: he

gave Administrative Inspections. An Administrative Inspection was a periodic dissection of the great body of paperwork amassed by each ship in the course of the year, and combined the sheer physical activity of a fire sale at Ohrbach's with the moral aspects of the Judgment Day. Short of engaging in a pitched battle with an enemy fleet, there was no better way to change your relative status on a promotion list than to meet Oliver Bintle head-on in an Administrative Inspection. Most naval officers thought they knew Naval Regulations backwards and forwards, but the backwaters of the Eastern seaboard were strewn with the wrecked careers of men who had challenged Bintle on an administrative point. Bintle rarely lost.

On the morning of the dreadful day, Bintle would show up bright and early with a picked team of trouble-shooters. Bintle had been collecting his team for years and he coached them personally. The members of the team would descend on the ship and fan out in all directions. Paint would be lifted in voids unentered for months, and chipping irons would get down to bare metal that had not seen the light of day since the ship came off the ways. Every piece of machinery on the ship, bar none, would be turned over, and woe to the gear that failed to operate and the man responsible for it. We had, stowed in a dark corner of the tank deck, a large metal box with a hole in the top and a crank on the side. The label plate read "Reverse Modifier Mark III. Do not operate handle with Circuit Z energized." No one knew what it was and no one would give us permission to throw it away. Gruber once discovered that if you put a carrot in the hole and turned the handle it came back out looking like a chrysanthemum, and the only time we ever used it was for buffet dinners in the wardroom. This had barely satisfied Bintle the last time he visited us and he was undoubtedly going to bring it up again in the future.

After everything had been inspected, the ship would be subjected to a harrowing inventory check. Everything had to be counted and had to check against the stock tally cards. This wasn't too hard with things like typewriters and stopwatches and binoculars, but when it came to such items as foul-weather mittens, cups, flashlight batteries or paintbrushes, it was a different story. Tiffany's stock control would have broken down on flashlight batteries.

The final item was Emergency Drills. Fire, and Abandon Ship were the usual ones, although Bintle had been known to call for Repel Boarders and, once, Lighten Ship. Lighten Ship was designed for last-ditch emergencies and involved, among other things, unbolting all the gun mounts and throwing the guns overboard. The ship Bintle pulled this one on didn't actually throw the guns away, but they had to go into a yard for a week out of turn to put everything back together.

After all the gear and the records had been scrutinized, and the drills completed, the inspecting party would retire to unused staterooms and spend an hour or so composing their reports. During this period the ship's officers sat in the wardroom, swilled black coffee, and made what passed for light conversation. Occasionally an inspector would stick his head in and ask for a copy of Naval Regulations, Knight's *Modern Seamanship*, or Roget's *Thesaurus*. The Naval Regulations the ship produced were invariably the wrong edition, and Bintle himself once caused a Supply Officer to pass out cold by appearing in the wardroom at this stage of the game and grimly requesting a copy of the Virginia Penal Code.

When all the reports were completed, a critique was held in the wardroom. This was supposed to be highly constructive and was known as "the wash-up." All the inspectors got up in turn, read out a list of the discrepancies they had uncovered in their departments, added a general status report, and gave their estimation of the time the ship would need to remedy the deficiencies. These reports were models of incisive prose, and if a member of the team seemed to be losing any of his ability as a writer, Bintle would at once make him sign up for a correspondence course in composition. By two o'clock in the afternoon all the inspectors would be gone, leaving the impression that the ship would probably be turned down if offered to the Lower Slobbovian Navy, and it was usually close to midnight before any of the ship's officers were in shape to do anything but paw feebly at cigarettes.

It took a good six weeks to get a ship ready for such an ordeal. It took a fortnight alone to count the foul-weather mittens. And Oliver Bintle was coming in seventeen days.

CHAPTER 6

IT was a glorious morning. The sun was shining on the Little Creek jetty as we pulled in, the air was brisk, and there was a telephone booth right at the end of the pier. The booth was empty, and I had been collecting change all week.

As soon as we were secured, I left the ship with El Toro. El Toro had been causing trouble. He had appropriated the forward end of the tank deck and had been sharpening his horns on the Reversé Modifier. He had got one horn in the hole and then had accidentally stepped on the handle, which had sort of frazzled the horn and apparently given him a headache; after that he wouldn't let anybody near the Reverse Modifier and we had to get at it for the Administrative Inspection. I was under strict instructions from Captain O'Gara to get rid of El Toro and it didn't matter where.

I led the goat up to the telephone booth and secured him to a nearby bollard. The booth was still empty. A sailor who had started for it stopped, exchanged a single hard look with El Toro, and retreated.

I put in a dime and the operator answered.

"Long distance? Little Hominy, ring two, please."

There was a moment's stunned silence.

"Where?"

"Little Hominy. It's in North Carolina. Not far from Big Hominy."

"Can I call you back?"

"Sure. Sure, take your time. I know how these things are."

I hung up and lit a cigarette. El Toro, with designs on the butt, tiptoed nearer and shivered.

The sailor came back. He sidled past the goat and entered the booth. There he had a long conversation with a girl who was apparently below the age of consent and deaf. The sailor finally left. I gave the butt to El Toro and lit another cigarette. Finally the phone rang.

"Hello? Hello? Sally?"

A hoarse voice answered. I could hardly recognize my operator.

"I found it," she rasped triumphantly. "I found it. It was right there in North Carolina all the time. I'm ringing it now."

So she was. There were two faraway buzzes and then the clatter of what sounded like a good half-dozen receivers being lifted. Someone breathed heavily. There was a muffled sneeze.

"Sally?"

"She'll be on in a minute, honey," a friendly voice said. "I just saw her go by coming back from town with the mail, and I doubt she's had time to take her coat off yet. You her new beau from New York?"

"Hello? Hello? Who is this?"

Another receiver was lifted. A lovely, thrilling voice said, "Hello?"

"Darling!"

"Wait a minute. Thank you very much, you all." Receivers clicked.

"Are we alone?"

"I think so. You never can tell."

"Will you marry me?"

"How was Puerto Rico?"

"Hot. Will you?"

"I'm thinking it over."

"Is this good?"

"There are possibilities."

"I could get a license. Just in case."

"I hardly know you. Only that you're in the Navy."

"It's nice, steady work."

"Always at sea."

"We get in once in a while. Refueling, inspections, things like that."

"I still don't know much about you."

"I have other talents. I juggle oranges."

"Look, why don't you come down this weekend? I've told my editor I'm doing a piece on rural libraries and their response to the challenge of television."

"I'll be there Friday. Don't go away."

"I'm rooted."

There was another muffled sneeze.

"*Gesundheit!*" I yelled. "It should be pneumonia!"

Sally said "Goodbye" and hung up.

I got the operator.

"How much?"

"I don't know," she wailed. "I can't find it in the toll book."

I gave her my address, and she promised to send a bill. When I left the booth, El Toro was halfway through the classified directory.

We went downtown. We had to walk, because the bus wouldn't let us aboard. I wanted to unload El Toro and then arrange for transportation to Little Hominy.

The S.P.C.A., where we stopped first, said they were only equipped to handle *small* animals, and would I please

take that monster away before he cleaned out all the files.

The airlines said Big Hominy had a field, because it was on an old list of emergency landing strips, but it wasn't marked on any of their maps, and there were certainly no commercial flights into it.

The Atlantic, Piedmont, and Beauregard Railroad didn't have an office in Norfolk. None of the other railroad companies had even heard of it. They hadn't heard of either Hominy, either. A Civil War buff in one office, however, *had* heard of it. He was positive that all eight miles of track had been torn up by 'Cump Sherman in Sixty-five.

The bus people could at least get me to Lye, Virginia,

• *111*

and, according to them, both Hominies were somewhere in the vicinity. Not only that, they offered to take El Toro off my hands. Handled goats all the time, they said. I checked him in the baggage room, left a carton of cigarettes with the attendant, and told him I'd be back Friday.

The first bus I could catch Friday evening got into Lye at 10:48. In order to get back on time Monday I would have to leave Lye on Sunday evening at 11:03. I bought four round-trip tickets and sent Sally a telegram asking her to meet me in Lye Friday. The telegram was returned to me the following week, undelivered, with an astringent note about fictitious addresses, but Sally knew the bus system and met the logical one anyway.

The Captain was doubtful. Desertion, he called it. Oliver Bintle due in two weeks and I wanted to go gallivanting off to some godforsaken hamlet in the Ozarks.

"Appalachians. I'll work nights."

"Desertion. Rank desertion."

"The books are in pretty good shape."

"Brown Bagger. That's what you are. You and Rudolph."

I winced.

I worked nights. We all worked nights. We painted the whole ship and we made out three new Divisional Training Courses. We revised the Watch, Quarter and Station Bill, the Abandon Ship Bill, and the Battle Bill. We tried the Repel Boarders Bill and surreptitiously loosened the nuts on the gun mounts. We even made out a Library Bill that would have done the Widener proud. The ship's library had fifty-seven books, not counting the collected fragments of Mickey Spillane, and there was a letter from the Captain appointing Rudolph Rush Library Officer. During the last Administrative Inspection Bintle had found this letter and cornered Rudolph, who was trying to explain the Reverse Modifier to someone else. Bintle had questioned Rudolph for thirty-five minutes, mostly about the Dewey Decimal System. Rudolph, who had his hands full, thought it had something to do with the binomial theorem, and he and Bintle had gotten into a frightful wrangle. This time, Rudolph knew the entire Dewey Decimal System cold, and could furthermore name all fifty-seven books, alphabetically by titles, alphabetically by authors, and in chronological order by Dewey numbers. He also knew who had checked out which books for the last six months and how long they had kept them.

I personally inventoried all the foul-weather gear, counted the 218 pairs of mittens twice, and locked them and the flashlight batteries in the Captain's safe, after changing the combination. We corrected all the charts, including the first eight hundred miles of the Amazon River. We washed and ironed all the signal bunting, and brought our stock of foreign flags up to date. Every once in a while a Navy ship finds itself in a foreign port when a local holiday is being celebrated, or a visiting ship is celebrating a holiday, and American ships fly the foreign flag in honor of the occasion. A Union Jack and a Tricolor will usually get you through most overseas trips, and if anyone else is celebrating you can always slip ashore and borrow the necessary flag from the local authorities. Bintle, however, always checked the flag locker, and usually asked to see flags from places like Yemen, Cambodia, and the Orange Free State. He once marked down another LST because their Saudi Arabian flag had "Allah" misspelled.

The Pharmacist's Mate locked himself into sick bay and polished it until it shone. All Pharmacist's Mates on ships which do not carry doctors are hand-picked, but Jack the Stitcher stood out even in a hand-picked group. As a very junior corpsman he had once assisted at an emergency appendectomy underway, and the ambition of his life was to undertake such a project himself. The advent of penicillin effectively removed any such opportunity, but it was a brave man who reported to him with an abdominal complaint when we were more than four hours from port. The Stitcher invariably referred to sick bay as "Surgery" and spent most of his spare time honing a large collection of scalpels. The only member of the crew who was not afraid of him was Shrieking Eagle, because the Stitcher had once tripped on a ladder and creamed himself, and Shrieking Eagle, a shaman in his own right, had sewed *him* up with nylon fishing line.

The only man who intimidated the Stitcher was Dr. Bredonstard, Bintle's Medical Inspector, who had once recommended prefrontal lobotomies for the Captain and four officers of a ship he was inspecting. It lay within

Bredonstard's power to transfer the Stitcher to a shore hospital, where he would become just another corpsman and no longer the head of a ship's medical department, so we never had to worry about Surgery for inspections. The Stitcher spent all day there inventorying his scalpels and cleaning up. No one was allowed in. Toothache, compound fractures, or Tsutsugamushi fever, there was nothing available but Band-aids.

By Friday the ship was spotless. Even the Captain was mollified. At five o'clock I was in the bus, with a brown bag borrowed from Murdoch Kutley on the rack over my head and El Toro out behind in a small trailer.

Precisely at 10:48 we pulled into Lye. I found Sally sitting at the lunch counter in the bus station drinking coffee between two teen-agers. The one on the right was engrossed in *Will Acting Spoil Elvis Presley?* and the one on the left was reading *The Real Jimmy Dean Story*. Sally was reading *General Education in a Free Society*, in a plain wrapper.

"The only way to educate them is to start them young," I said, reading over her shoulder and scowling so ferociously at the Presley aficionado that she slid over one place and left me a seat. "It's easier if you have your own, and, things being the way they are, you save yourself a lot of trouble by having them in wedlock."

"Hi," Sally said. "Background reading. My TV article."

"Nonsense. Pure rationalization. You're thinking along the right lines. Will you marry me?"

The Jimmy Dean fan put her magazine down.

"You just got here," Sally said.

"Why waste time? Will you?"

"I'm still thinking."

I shrugged my shoulders. The magazine was picked up again.

I paid Sally's check and she led the way to a vintage station wagon. We got in.

"You may have to get out and push," Sally said, inserting the key, but the engine shuddered into life at the fifth attempt, and we rolled out of Lye with the isinglass curtains flapping in the night air.

"On to Little Hominy!" I exclaimed brightly.

Sally made a sharp turn off the concrete highway onto what seemed to be a plank road. The car plunged into an apparently solid wall of underbrush and shouldered its way through.

"That's the really important turn," Sally yelled over the noise of branches scraping along our flanks. "Isn't used much, and very easy to miss."

I held on to the seat. After a while the shrubbery thinned out, and the road wound in and out of a series of low hills. Occasionally a log-and-mud barn loomed up, ornamented with posters for Bull Durham chewing tobacco, Sweet Scotch Snuff, and something called Miles' Nervine. A tattered political poster featured a face with a startling resemblance to Alf Landon, but I could have been mistaken.

There was a sudden change in the vibrations, as if every other plank had been removed. I pulled out my cigarette lighter and inspected the road map, but all pretense to respectable cartography had been abandoned at the outskirts of Lye.

"North Carolina state line," Sally said. "We use bigger logs."

The car bounded a few hundred yards through shallow water and stopped. Rabbits' eyes glowed at us from hummocks, and the stygian night billowed in around the pulsating headlights.

"Big Hominy," Sally said. "I thought you might like to see."

I looked. The left headlight vaguely illuminated a small signboard attached to a wooden building that might have passed for a grand-piano crate. I got out to inspect. There was an inch and a half of water on the road.

"Bug Lake," Sally said. "We cross it on the way home. You still want to marry me?"

"I'm thinking," I said, and splashed over to the building, which had neither windows nor, apparently, a door. The sign said "Big Hominy. Elevation 423 feet. No mail given out after sundown."

"Where's the airport?"

"You're standing on it. That's the control tower."

I got back in without comment, and we started off again. The road improved slightly, and there were six-inch shoulders descending to wet clay.

"Look," I finally asked, "does your mother like it down here, all by herself?"

"Oh, sure. Weyman looks after us. He's a terrific cook and a first-rate butler. And Mama broke him in as a chaperon for me. He got a long list of instructions from her about you, before she left. She's spending the weekend in Charleston. You better not hold my hand or anything."

"Tell me about your home," I said firmly. The Cape jessamines had to make their appearance sometime, and so far the countryside was straight out of Arthur Rackham.

"Bustard's Roost," Sally began, "was built in 1836 by Captain Wade Stubblefield. He was my great-grandfather. The family lived there until the Battle of Big Hominy, in 1864. The house wasn't exactly burned, but the Hominy Greys made a charge that ended in the library, so the family moved away. You can still see the hoof marks. In 1909 my grandfather, Jefferson Stubblefield, broke the bank at Monte Carlo, and he fixed the house up again. The family moved back, and on and off they've lived there ever since. Whenever they had a good crop they went abroad. Then my sister and I started having to go to boarding school and college and things, and Mama said she'd better stay home for a while. My father didn't leave much to raise us on. Now that I'm working and Daphne has only one more year at Radcliffe, Mama's taken to traveling again."

The road grew smoother, and I realized we were on a graveled drive. Great oaks spread around us in the darkness and then a light up ahead showed four massive white columns. I sat up and felt better.

"Welcome to Bustard's Roost."

I got out Murdoch's bag and started up the steps and at the front door I was assaulted. It weighed almost as much as I did, and was white, with black spots.

"Get down, Sugar Plum!"

"Sugar? Plum?" I got up, as soon as it took its paws off my chest.

"He was a right cute puppy, and Mama named him Sugar Plum."

Sugar Plum wagged his tail. The night air whistled at every cut.

"Does it ever bite?" I felt my ribs.

"No, he just stomps on people. He bit a car once, a convertible. We had to buy the man a new top."

"Nice doggy," I said, and reached up and patted it.

Weyman was waiting at the door. Considering his height, which was about six feet four, and his build, which was solid, he was not precisely what I imagined old family retainers looked like. He gave me a long, hard inspection, and then reached out and took my bag.

"The lieutenant will be quartered on the second deck, just aft of the telephone stand," he said. I had apparently passed the test, but in my surprise I hardly noticed that.

"You weren't . . . by any chance. . . ?" I began.

"Chief Steward. Went out on twenty," Weyman said briefly, taking my bag upstairs.

It was very late, and I said good night to Sally and started upstairs myself. I had every intention of kissing her good night, but a warning, noncommittal cough from the landing above stopped me. Sally smiled sweetly.

When I got to my room, Sugar Plum was stretched out across the foot of the bed, watching Weyman unpack the bag. I took my coat off and started to hang it up.

"Lieutenant? What is your intentions, sir?"

"Eh? What intentions?"

"Towards Miss Sally, sir. Is your intentions honorable?"

"Good God, man, of course they are. Now look here, I know you got instructions from her mother, but if you think—"

"My instructions from Miss Sally's mother, Lieutenant, was to find out what was your intentions, and then leave you two alone. That girl never could make up her mind."

Mother-in-law, Consolidated shares went up about six points. I stared at Weyman.

"I figured they was honorable, Lieutenant," he went on. "Them that gets as far as Bustard's Roost usually is. I just thought I'd ask. Good night, sir, and the best of luck in the morning."

Weyman left, but Sugar Plum stayed on the bed and smiled at me when I made shooing motions. His smile was all fangs and gullet, so I curled up at the other end of the bed and made myself as comfortable as I could.

In the morning Weyman stuck his head in and said "Pssst, Lieutenant. Reveille, sir." When he brought the grits and bacon in to the breakfast table he looked as if he'd never seen me before in his life.

After breakfast Sally and I went into the library, and I went right back to proposing. It looked like a short week-end, and I didn't want to waste any time. Since one purpose of this volume is to provide a few words of cheer for the groom, that forgotten man of modern marriage, it might be well at this point to comment on the initial step of his harried journey—the proposal. It is difficult, although by no means impossible, to get yourself engaged *without* proposing, but I have neither the space nor the experience to go into that here. The precise wording is something every groom must settle for himself. Proposals, however, are by no means over once the question has in whatever fashion been asked, despite the sense of giddy relief the male experiences in having the damned thing out in the open. The battle in most cases is just getting underway.

Proposals are deceptively simple questions and can be met with deceptive, simple answers. "Yes" and "No" are the only ones the male is at all prepared for, but they are rarely encountered. (I am now drawing on Schuyler's experience as well as my own.) "I dunno," "What did you say?" or even "Me? Marry you?" are all logical responses and clearly indicate the prevailing atmosphere. But something in the female mind is repelled by anything so cut-and-dried, and these answers too are on the proscribed list. The chosen reply is rarely short and usually laden with complex ramifications.

Proposals involve two distinct questions—the primary psychological one of "Shall I?" and the purely mechanical one of "*When* shall I?" The catch lies in the fact that the female mind is seemingly incapable of resisting the temptation of toying with the possibilities of the second question before it is willing to admit that it has in fact answered the first question. It is for this reason that so many straightforward proposals are met with a disconcerting discourse on "Why I can't possibly marry you in September."

The male, groping through the bewildering cloud of reason, always returns to the nub.

"But you *will* marry me, yes?" It has become an obsession with him.

The groom at this point is in a sorry pickle, although it is as nothing compared to the pickle he will presently be marinating in. The female mind is not to be fenced in. "I didn't say anything of the sort," it answers, returning with zest to the relative merits of a marriage around, say, Thanksgiving, as compared with a really big production at Christmas.

The groom is stymied. He feels engaged. She seems to be acting engaged. She even sounds engaged. She will not, however, admit that she *is* engaged. She just likes to play with the idea. The fact that every thrilling dangle she gives the idea has the hapless male reeling like a yo-yo does not seem to penetrate. Since he has said his little piece, and has not been told to go away, the conclusion seems obvious to him. All that remains is to get a "yuh" out of her, or, failing that, force her to admit to a disinterested third party that she has been proposed to and is still on speaking terms with the proposer.

Madness lies in any attempt to hurry the situation. In her own good time she will let him know and she will let other people know. Rudolph Rush claims that the first official confirmation he had was a letter from an engraving firm, checking on his middle name. When he asked what they wanted his middle name for (it was Sebastian) they told him for the announcements, of course. Elvira had him pretty groggy by that time, so it was only when he wrote again and asked *what* announcements that he found out the good news. The point for the groom to remember is that while he still has a fight on his hands, the pot is all but his. He is holding a straight flush.

After I stopped proposing, Sally said she had to work on her article, so I borrowed the station wagon. Big Hominy I had to see in broad daylight. Weyman gave me the keys and asked me how everything was going.

"Just give her time," he said. "It's like I told you."

Big Hominy was slightly more pretentious than it had seemed the night before. The control tower was also a gas pump; you got down off the tower and lifted the lid off. There was also a second shack, a combination lunch room and waiting room, if you counted the bench next to it. The airfield itself was a long grassy strip next to Bug Lake with five cows grazing on it.

The lunch room and post office was tended by a sprightly

man in his sixties, wearing an ancient leather helmet with glassless goggles pushed up on his forehead. I got a Dixie Pig Bar-B-Q sandwich (it was all he had) and a glass of buttermilk. Then I inspected the field.

"Much activity here?"

"Jenny landed in Twenty-four, but it took right off again. Then along about Thirty-seven an Army fighter circled me twicet. Sure thought *he* was coming in—he was on fire— but I guess the cows sort of scared him off. He crashed about three miles west of Little Hominy."

"Hardly seems worth keeping the place open."

The ancient glared at me. "Sonny, this is a historical field. America's oldest operational airport."

"No."

"Fact. The Wright boys came through here on their way to Kitty Hawk. Spent about six hours here, waiting for a connection on the Ay, Pee and Bee, before they found out about the track. Wilbur hisself told me, mighty good place for an airport. I didn't even know what one was. They unpacked that crate of theirs, put it together, and made a twenty-yard hop, right over there in the south corner, next to that Holstein. Orville said it wasn't going to be long before aeroplanes was a-zooming all over the country. I was eighteen then, but I bought this pasture that very evening and set up business. Ain't been many aeroplanes, but I make a right nice living off the gas pump and this here snack bar, what with folks stopping in to pick up their mail. Have another Dixie Pig."

When I got back to Bustard's Roost it was getting dark. Weyman served our supper, and then I proposed for a while again. Weyman showed up once or twice without warning and inquired blandly, "Did you ring, Lieutenant?" and Sally smiled smugly each time, but Weyman winked at me on the way out.

"Is this boring you?" I finally asked her. "I mean, just say so, and I'll stop for now."

"No-o-o," Sally said. "I'm not bored. But tell me more about your ship. Just where is it going to be, say, around Easter?"

I told her, and she stared dreamily into the fire and started to count on her fingers.

"What did you say?" I yelled.

"May. I mean June. I mean nothing. I didn't say anything at all."

It was the most encouraging sign to date. I plunged into the fray with renewed zeal and got off a half-dozen proposals in as many minutes. After a particularly noteworthy effort, Sugar Plum came over and licked my hand.

"I think he likes you," Sally said, getting me a towel.

"Love you, love your dog."

I was making progress.

CHAPTER 7

LATE Sunday night Sally delivered me back to the bus terminal in Lye. We had no sooner arrived than the manager rushed out. He was furious.

"Aha!" he yelled.

I looked blank.

"Abandoning goats, are we?"

"My God! El Toro! I forgot all about him!"

"No human being who ever spent more than eleven seconds within one mile of that beast could possibly forget him. What the hell was the big idea?"

"I forgot him. I had something else on my mind. I couldn't unload him in Norfolk." The manager paused for breath and I remembered O'Gara's parting instructions.

"How would you like him," I tried, "as a present?"

The manager, it developed, did not in any case want a goat, and under no circumstances wanted to have anything further to do with the particular noisome specimen now laying waste (I winced) to the baggage room.

I turned to Sally. "Darling, do you think Weyman would like a goat?"

She was quite firm about it.

El Toro and I arrived in Norfolk early in the morning. The baggage room there was closed, so we took a taxi out to Little Creek together. There was a little trouble with El Toro at the gate, until I pointed out that I would have no objections whatsoever to leaving him in the guardhouse and letting the sentry explain about him to his commanding officer when he showed up. The sentry thought this one over for a minute, and then decided that nothing in his standing orders specifically prohibited goats, so he let us through.

When I got to the ship I turned him loose on the tank deck to graze and sat down in my stateroom to plan my speech to Captain O'Gara.

I had just put a polish on the opening phrases (My, that's a nice-looking uniform you have on this morning, sir. Funny thing happened to me last night . . .") when the door burst open and the Captain himself bounded in. He had a dispatch in his hands.

"Bintle! Bintle! He's coming! In ten minutes! Bintle!"

"My, that's a nice-looking uniform you have on this . . . Cap'n, he's not due till Thursday."

"Changed! All changed! Surprise inspection! Surprise! Surprise! In whites! Ten minutes! With white gloves!"

He danced out. I could hear people running all over the ship and whistles blowing. Lownes dashed by with clean sheets and a mop. Chief Popper's voice blasted out of the P.A. system, repeating "Now hear this!" over and over again.

I was galvanized. I grabbed a clean white uniform and started to wrestle my way into it. Bintle always specified out-of-season uniforms, because very few people ever had all the proper accouterments together. I was halfway into the blouse when I remembered the buttons, so I pulled it off and started to put them in. While I was putting them in Lownes came in, pulled off my dirty pillowcase, looked wildly around, and finally stuffed it into the bottom drawer on my desk. As he ran out there was a clicking over the loudspeaker, a moment's silence, and then the Captain's voice.

"All hands! Bintle! Ten minutes! In whites! No shit now!"

I got the blouse on and was all the way down the passageway before I remembered the white gloves, and in turning around I careened off Rudolph and knocked my cap off. As I picked it up I saw it still had the blue cover on it. I got the cover changed, and ransacked the bureau looking for gloves. All I could find was one left glove and a note from Schuyler saying he had borrowed the other one. I pulled a white sock over my right hand and lit out for the quarterdeck. As I emerged from the stateroom I collided full tilt with Schuyler. He was all dressed except for the bottom half of a pair of red-and-yellow-striped pajamas. I pointed at him.

"Pants!"

He pointed at me.

"Shoes! Socks!"

He disappeared down the passageway, and I returned to my stateroom, tore off my black shoes and socks, got out my white shoes, and started hunting for another pair of white socks. There weren't any. I got out a package of Band-aids, covered as much of my ankles as I could, put on the shoes, and started for the quarterdeck.

Commander Oliver Bintle and his inspection party were coming up the pier.

It was an awesome sight.

Oliver Bintle in repose looked like a mother rhinoceros about to start to the rescue of her imperiled child. Behind him and in step strode his party, looking neither to the right nor to the left.

First was Dr. Bredonstard, with a small field microscope in one hand and a butterfly net in the other.

Next to him was Lieutenant Magerowski, the Engineer-

ing Inspector, with a crowbar jauntily slung over one shoulder.

Behind him was Lieutenant Commander Anthony, the Administration and Organization Inspector, staggering under the weight of two bulging briefcases.

The Inspection Party came up the gangway, the side-boys snapped to attention, and everybody saluted as the boatswain's pipe shrilled out. (The correct call, thank heaven. There had been the week Shrieking Eagle was learning to play "Pretty Redwing.")

The Captain dropped his salute, stepped forward, and

tripped over a civilian who was standing on the quarter-deck.

"I'm Professor Deininger," the civilian started, helping O'Gara up.

"Later, please," the Captain said, putting out his hand to greet Commander Bintle. Bintle ignored the hand and counted the side-boys.

"Make a note of that," he growled at Anthony. As soon as we were dismissed I dashed into the ship's office and spent a frantic six minutes looking up the correct number of side-boys for a commander. We had the right number. I returned triumphantly to the wardroom just in time to hear Bintle complain to the Captain that it was just too damn bad when an Executive Officer didn't bother to come to the wardroom to meet the Senior Inspector.

I stepped forward and shook hands with Commander Bintle. The sock caught in the catch of his ID bracelet and pulled off as I dropped my hand. He didn't see it for a minute or two, and when he did look in it, it had the Captain's name tape sewn inside.

We passed out coffee and everybody smiled at the commander. The civilian peered into the wardroom, looked around, and came up to Commander Bintle.

"I am Professor Deininger," he began again. "I represent the National Ichthyological Foundation. Is there a Mr. Shrieking E. Garfield in your employ?"

"What? Who?"

The Captain stepped forward.

"I think maybe he wants me, sir. Yes, Mr. Garfield is a member of this command. What's he . . . What do you want?"

The professor's face shone with a zealot's delight.

"I have here a certified check for $50,000 made out to Mr. Garfield. Where is the *latimeria chalumnae*?"

It was the Captain's turn.

"Who? What?"

"Our coelacanth." He pulled out a picture. "This is your Mr. Garfield, is it not?"

The Captain inspected the snapshot. It was Vlasser's picture of Shrieking Eagle and the fish he caught off Vieques.

"Yeah, that's Shrieking Eagle. Say, that's quite a fish. Where'd you get this?"

"It was forwarded to me by the editor of *Reel and Creel*. It arrived in Friday's mail. Our directors met over the weekend and we are prepared to offer $50,000 to Mr. Garfield. Judging from the photograph, his specimen is in superior condition to either of the other two known specimens. This represents, of course, *latimeria*'s first appearance in Atlantic waters. Oh, this is a great day for American ichthyology!"

"Say, what the hell is all this?" Bintle asked. The Captain opened his mouth. Then he shut it. Schuyler moved forward and took the professor by the elbow.

"Excuse me, Captain. I think I can help the gentleman." He steered the professor to a corner of the wardroom.

"Professor," he began, "there is something you should know. I hardly know how to tell you."

Bintle pulled himself together. "Okay, boys. Let's get this show on the road."

Dr. Bredonstard carefully poured some of his coffee into a test tube, plugged it with a wisp of cotton, and stuck it in his breast pocket.

Magerowski stood up and grasped his crowbar. He had changed to dungarees and hip boots. Drawing on leather gauntlets and loosely knotting a bandanna around his throat, he turned to Murdoch.

"Shall we go?" he asked nonchalantly. Murdoch faltered out after him.

Anthony turned to me.

"Let's get this over with, sonny," he said.

We started for the ship's office. Just then a shrill scream arose from the corner of the wardroom. Professor Deininger was clutching the arms of his chair, his body rigid and his face a mask of horror. Schuyler was making soothing noises and patting his arm in sympathy.

"The *entire* coelacanth? Raw?" The Professor collapsed, put his face in his hands, and started to sob.

In the course of the next hour I learned things about our filing system the existence of which I had never even suspected. There was an order, issued in 1847, about whale oil for spare running lights, which Anthony was able to prove had never been rescinded. My training program for quartermasters was, in his phrase, "grossly inadequate," because the duty quartermaster did not know the proper fog signal for an auxiliary steamer in international waters proceeding under sail with the smokestack and paddle wheels unrigged. I lost points when it developed that I didn't know if the genitive plural of "court-martial" was "courts'-martial," "court's-martials," or "court-martials'." According to Anthony, if this was any sample of the way I ran a ship's office, it was a bloody wonder I hadn't found out sooner.

When I opened the safe, there were three hundred and twenty-four right foul-weather mittens, twenty-eight left foul-weather mittens, and a dead mouse in the flashlight battery box. This was obviously the work of poltergeists. My protests that there were only eleven men required to be topside at any given time in a duty status were unavailing.

"Your Evacuation Bill," Anthony pointed out, "despite its numerous shortcomings, correctly provides for two hundred and fifty-six helpless, freezing refugees. You trying to give someone frostbite?"

A distant hammering arose from the engine room. Shortly thereafter Murdoch tottered by the office door, with his uniform soiled and tattered. He was holding half a crowbar.

Once Bintle stuck his head in. His shoes and trousers were sopping.

"Who," he asked in an ominous tone, "is in charge of that soft-drink machine?"

The Fire Drill was a shambles. To lend veracity to the proceedings, Bintle put a bucket with oily rags in it in the officers' shower and lighted it. We were to be marked on how long it took the smoke to be noticed and on what action would be taken by whoever did the noticing, as well as on our extinguishing efforts.

In a few minutes the entire passageway was filled with smoke and Bintle was glowering out of the shower stall over a stop watch.

The first man to enter was Lownes. He took one look at the bucket, yelled "Fire!" and started for the quarterdeck to hit the alarm.

Bintle caught him by the shoulder.

"You have been overcome by smoke. You are a casualty. Lie down in the passageway."

Lownes lay down. Visibility was decreasing rapidly. A messenger from the radio shack groped his way along the passageway and handed the message board to the Captain. He had to step over Lownes.

Bintle howled at him.

"You see a fire, man! Aren't you going to do anything about it?"

The messenger licked his lips and coughed. He looked at Bintle, then at the bucket.

"I'll go get someone, sir. I'm new here."

In a minute he was back with Shrieking Eagle.

Bintle reached out of his stall and grabbed him by the elbow.

"There's a fire here! Emergency! What are you going to do?"

Shrieking Eagle looked at Bintle, then at the bucket. Then he shrugged, reached into the stall, and turned on the shower.

After Bintle had changed again, we met in the wardroom and he announced that there would be an Abandon Ship Drill and that it had better be a good one.

Except for Professor Deininger, the wardroom was quiet. Schuyler was leading him out, a broken man.

"But the depth? The temperature? The salinity? Does he even know what sex it was?"

"Like I told you, Professor, it was just off Vieques. A real hot day."

"Could I talk to him? He must remember something. Even what it tasted like would be a help."

"Sure, Professor," Schuyler said. "We'll go talk to him. By the way, how's your Chickasaw?"

Bintle went to make his preparations and we sat and waited. Abandon Ship Drills were notorious reputation-smashers. It was something like a race. Just before the drill started, Bintle would grab a member of the crew at random and hide him in the Captain's head. The drill was then started and Bintle held a stop watch on us. The stop watch was stopped as soon as we could name the man who had been hidden, an identification that was technically made possible by mustering the rest of the crew to find out who was missing.

The trouble was that when the drill got under way a very large number of stations had to be manned. The bulk of the crew fell in at quarters, where we could count noses, but there were small groups all over the ship, lowering boats, destroying confidential papers, securing engineering spaces, and collecting provisions and navigational equipment. People on leave had other people substituting for them, fourteen men were ready to swear they had seen Joe Abernathy two minutes before the drill started (and four days after he had been transferred), and Gruber was invariably baking a pie and would claim he didn't hear the word passed.

Executive Officers on small ships could reduce the number of missing people to about four names in very short order. They would then instigate a frenzied search for them, while the Captain grew purple, danced on the bridge, tried to look over Bintle's shoulder at the stop watch, and would finally grab the P.A. system and start yelling "Now the Executive Officer lay up to the bridge on the double." What happened when Bintle inspected a large carrier with, say, three thousand men I couldn't even begin to imagine.

Bintle, moreover, never played fair. Sometimes he hid two men and once he didn't hide any. Twice he hid the Captain, and both ships on which this happened had to give up after half an hour. Finding the missing man in five minutes was regarded as outstanding; anything over fifteen minutes was unsatisfactory.

Now, I have never had to abandon a ship, and I sincerely hope I never do, but if the situation ever does arise I doubt if there will be time for that muster. We once had a movie aboard called *In Which We Serve*, a World War II picture about the Royal Navy that starred Noel Coward. The picture opened with a British destroyer under air attack and before the first reel was five minutes old, Mr. Coward, as the skipper, was forced to shrug his shoulders and pass the word "Abandon ship!" When a Royal Navy commander says "Abandon" he means just that, and our crew watched with open mouths. There was none of this nonsense about counting noses. British tars dove overboard in platoon formation, boats went down, life rings zipped by, and that was that. Mr. Coward, in the finest nautical tradition, floated off the bridge with great aplomb. The camera followed him down as he sank, fathom after fathom, with his eyes closed and his hand firmly clutching his nose. The screen started to blur. Apparently Mr. Coward was done for. At that point it is customary for a man's past life to flash before his eyes, but, since Mr. Coward was a Royal Navy commander, instead of his own life he started to review the life of his ship, thus leading into an uncommonly fine picture. As the darkness thickened and the music was getting terribly dramatic, Captain O'Gara snorted fiercely.

"See?" he rasped. "Still waiting for his goddam muster!"

This time, however, we had taken precautions. I had my fingers crossed. Bintle looked at Anthony.

"All set?" he asked brightly. Bintle loved Abandon Ship Drills.

"Safe and sound," Anthony answered, dangling the key to the Captain's head.

"O'Gara, you are underway five hundred miles due south of St. Helena. You have just been rammed amidships to port by a Chris-craft cabin cruiser. The situation is hopeless. Abandon ship!" Bintle started the stop watch.

The word was passed and we all charged out on deck. The crew fell in at quarters and the petty officers raced through the muster and I kept praying that whoever was in the head would remember. The divisional petty officers reported to me and I wheeled to the bridge.

"Horowitz missing, sir!" I shouted.

Bintle's jaw dropped.

The Captain nudged him.

"The stop watch, sir."

Bintle stopped the stop watch. "Eighteen seconds," he croaked. "It's impossible. Get the man in the head."

A moment later Anthony appeared on the bridge. He had Shrieking Eagle with him.

"What," asked Bintle, "is your name?"

Shrieking Eagle turned around. Across the back of his dungaree shirt, in regulation letters with the paint still moist, was stenciled HOROWITZ, J. A.

The wash-up was a grim affair. Dr. Bredonstard read a gloomy report that gave the impression it could only be a matter of hours before bubonic plague was raging through the lower decks. The reference to a "failure to post adequate safety instructions for all galley equipment" had me stumped until Rudolph whispered, "The Reversifier. He stuck his finger in it." We were able to have the remark about "evidence of rodent infestation of a massive nature" removed only by producing El Toro in the wardroom and claiming he was the ship's mascot, a procedure that startled Captain O'Gara, who had no idea he was back.

Lieutenant Magerowski delivered an inspiring address on the future of American marine engineering, profusely illustrated with a collection of small brass screws and a magnifying glass, which he passed out among the audience.

"All from the soft-drink machine," Murdoch whispered to me hoarsely.

Bintle went down his check-off list. "Morale," he snapped. "I forgot to check morale."

He wheeled on Lownes, who was standing behind him with the coffee tray.

"Are you happy?" he bellowed.

"Sir?" The cups rattled and crashed.

"Are you *really* happy?"

"I'm feeling a mite poorly today, sir. I'm clean out of Miltown."

Lownes bent over to pick up the debris.

"Doesn't seem too sure of himself, does he, now?" Bintle asked the Captain.

The final mark was "Good." We had an all-Navy record in the Abandon Ship Drill, despite a small loss of points for our failure to pick up the crew of the Chris-craft, and Bintle knew when he was beaten.

The Inspection Party finally rolled off the ship, snarling at the quarterdeck watch as they went.

I looked at my watch. It was almost time for liberty. I thought of Lye. Wheels began to revolve. It was possible to get the evening bus, be in Lye by 10:48, catch the 11:03, and be back in Norfolk for morning quarters.

That left fifteen whole minutes in Lye. I could commute. On the way to the bus depot I called Sally.

"Darling!"

"You just left. What's the matter?"

"I'm coming back. Be in Lye at 10:48 tonight."

"Tonight?"

"Tonight. For God's sake don't fail me."

"I'll tell Weyman to make up the guest room for you again."

"Don't bother. There isn't time to explain. Just meet that bus."

I fell asleep as soon as we started. When I woke up it was one minute after eleven and we were just entering the Lye terminal. I was in a rear seat and it took almost a full minute for the passengers ahead of me to debus. The woman immediately in front of me had four large suitcases which she moved one after the other, three inches at a time. She was having her troubles with them because she was just about as wide as the aisle herself, and the suitcases were big enough to hold torsos. I tried to climb over the suitcases and she got mad and started to lecture me about shoving people. I tipped my hat and vaulted over the hurdle, lady, suitcases and all. From the door I saw Sally and, over her head, the return bus to Norfolk. It was full, the motor was running, and the driver had his hand on the door handle. I kissed Sally and started to trot across the terminal.

"I love you. Will you marry me?"

"Right now? Hey, slow down. Where you going?"

"I have to catch that bus. Will you marry me?" The door was beginning to swing shut.

"But you only just got here!"

"The bus was late. I should have had fifteen minutes." I got my foot in the door. "I'll be back tomorrow night, same time. Will you marry me?"

The bus driver twitched the door against my foot.

"Will you? You don't have to answer now. I'll be back tomorrow."

I kissed her and got on the bus and found a seat in the rear and pulled the window down. The bus started to roll. Sally loped alongside.

"You can't do this!" she yelled. "I have to drive twenty-five miles round trip and the tires won't stand it every night!"

"Will you marry me?" I yelled back. "I'll come every night till you say 'yes'!"

The bus was gathering speed and people all over the terminal were following events with interest. Somebody called out, "Go on, sister, marry him!" and others took it up. The fat lady shrilled, "Don't you do it! He's the rudest son of a bitch I ever saw!" and I stuck my tongue out at her.

Sally stood and glared at me as the bus pulled away. Just as we turned the first corner she stamped her foot and shouted, "Okay! Okay, dammit! I'll marry you!"

Everybody cheered. I pulled my head in. The people on the bus all applauded and the driver tooted the horn.

I was engaged.

CHAPTER 8

I got back aboard just in time for breakfast. I hadn't slept at all on the bus because two juniors from the University of Virginia had decided I should celebrate my engagement and had gotten off in South Hill and returned with a bottle and paper hats for all the passengers and the driver. It was a very nice party and the driver didn't complain until the square dancing started in the aisle. I still had the paper hat on when I entered the wardroom and I needed a shave.

"I'm engaged," I croaked.

"We're going to Greenland," the Captain said mournfully.

"The bus was late."

"We leave in two hours."

"I had less than a minute in Lye."

They had to shake me again.

The ship was not only going to Greenland, it was going to Naples afterwards, and it was going to stay there a year and a half. They had changed our home port. There were to be nine days between our return from Greenland and our departure for Naples, which was ample for a wedding and a honeymoon. Rudolph Rush, for example, got married at ten o'clock in the evening and left on maneuvers at midnight and didn't see his bride again for six weeks. Nine days was fat.

Before we left for New York, the first stop on the voyage north, I managed to get the essential details settled, although it took a great deal out of the telephone operator. Clearly, the wedding should follow as closely as possible on the ship's return from Greenland, and Sally refused to get married anywhere except Little Hominy.

"That way we have the railroads on *our* side" was the way she put it.

I wrote an appropriate note to my future mother-in-law and telegraphed my family in New York. Then I hastily ordered a miniature of my Naval Academy ring and sailed for New York with a clear conscience and a high heart.

I had heard tell of weddings being no end of bother, in some cases absolutely flattening (both psychologically and financially) both families and even innocent bystanders. All this fuss I could not understand. One became engaged, casually informed close relatives and perhaps a few old friends, got married and settled down. There was no reason why the whole thing should be placed in the public domain.

The trip to New York was quite uneventful and took less than forty-eight hours. We were to pick up some gear slated for the Air Force base at Thule, make a final effort to unload El Toro, and meet with representatives of the Navy Foul Weather Clothing Research and Development Program, who had something on their minds. As long as it wasn't mittens, we'd be happy to talk to them.

From the Navy Yard I took a subway home. I had no sooner entered the front door of my parents' apartment than I was abruptly disabused of all notions about calmness and simplicity in connection with weddings.

In all honesty, I had expected a warm, even hilarious reception, having lately reached that point in life where the adjective "confirmed" was apt to be coupled with the noun "bachelor." I had lately been the target of some blunt hints that it was time to start looking around, and my mother had developed an increasing preoccupation with other people's grandchildren. I anticipated approbation, not only in having come to the decision to marry but also for having chosen such a charming, intelligent and altogether remarkable bride. I was instead greeted like a congenital criminal whose latest escapade has not yet been confirmed but who has one hell of a crust in showing his face around decent society.

The major indictments against me, I discovered, were:

(a) having conducted the entire business *sub rosa*, so that tribal emotional participation had been practically nil; (b) having picked a date less than a month away; and (c) having managed to absent myself from the scene of turmoil until virtually the instant of the ceremony.

The last indictment was by far the most serious. I was given to understand that I was walking out on my responsibilities, leaving an unexpected crisis to be dealt with by noble and self-sacrificing relatives. The apartment was full of noble relatives and the telephone was going full blast to more relatives and a large number of unidentified commercial establishments. We had what amounted to open lines to Boston, Syracuse, and Little Rock, and lightning was going to strike in Little Hominy just as soon as the operator could find it.

Somehow I found a chair and put my bag down, which was a little difficult because all the chairs were full of parcels and magazines and relatives. I said hello to the relatives, moved the parcels, and looked at the magazines while interparliamentary debate raged over my head.

There was an astounding number of them (the magazines, that is), considering they were all about, by, for, or pertaining to brides. In thumbing through this trove of nuptial lore I was soon struck by the almost total lack of information provided for grooms. Grooms did occasionally show up in the photographs, usually as the nape of a well-barbered neck or a hand protruding from a morning coat.

They were clearly only a series of props on which a bride could support herself gracefully.

In both the advertising and the publishing worlds it is a tacit assumption that the groom's function in life is solely that of a catalyst. He is expected to ask one simple question, thereby setting into motion titanic forces, and then to stay decently out of sight until called upon to testify before all the world that the question has, in fact, been asked, doing so in two words and if possible without clearing his throat. This is an unrealistic attitude and someone should wise up the advertisers and publishers at once.

Grooms need help. They need advice. They are in desperate need of moral support. They can search high and low and will find nothing but low humor. They are virtually ignored on all sides. Their prospective brides appropriate their names and charge accounts and scamper about in a mad frenzy of activity. Their bachelor friends class their activity as high treason, and their married friends act as if this happened every day. Their parents are occupied with food, clothing, transportation, and protocol.

Until the ceremony, grooms can only sit around keeping out of the way of those with serious work to do, and make small red marks on calendars. If, as I was, they are in the Navy, they are suddenly confronted with the problem of equating the demands of the great civilian world to the limited amounts of time doled out by the services for non-professional activities. This at least has the merit of keeping them busy—so busy, in fact, that they sometimes find it hard to realize that they are going to be *married*, and they have even been known to get married to someone else while they were waiting. Grooms, in short, are a sorry lot, and it's high time someone rallied around and took them in hand.

I for one was forced to go the entire distance alone. I remember at one point realizing that the only wedding I had ever actually witnessed had been that of an uncle, which occurred when I was eight. There had been some kind of an argument about my drinking a glass of champagne, and even with my uncle on my side I lost out. I retained the distinct impression that his words carried no weight with anyone.

My knowledge of the subject was therefore limited to what I could glean from press clippings over the years, as my childhood friends succumbed one by one. These clippings always followed a set pattern, obviously unchanged since the days of the Medes and the Persians. They always began with a lengthy passage devoted to the blood lines of the bride. This section would carry her ancestry back as far as it was decently possible to go. Most families taking this tack petered out somewhere in the eighteenth century, although one lass of my acquaintance modestly admitted to descent from one "Dickon Smythe, Esquire, who fought under Drake at the defeat of the Armada."

Sally later admitted that she had outmaneuvered a great-aunt who blandly insisted that one branch of the female line could fairly safely be traced back to Charlemagne, by reminding her that the same branch had been terminated rather abruptly in an all-too-well-documented hanging for cattle-raising and offering to give the two items equal billing. The old lady evened the score by sending us a Doré Bible to Naples, where it could not conveniently be put into storage and the cost of mailing it home would have spelled financial ruin.

Pedigree firmly established, educational attainments were taken up next. This paragraph listed all pedagogical institutions attended right back to the years impinging on kindergarten. Those unable to muster a "was graduated from" saved face with a simple "attended." The face was greatly enhanced if either the Sorbonne or the University of Edinburgh could be mentioned. Hopeless nitwits had to be content with "was privately tutored."

Then followed a long sartorial orgy, in extreme cases going as far as the ushers' underwear. After this came a long list of the relatives and comrades who had been raked in for the festivities, each name backstopped with degree of kinship and place of origin.

Finally, if the newsprint shortage was not in an acute stage, the World Series was over, and no crime involving a sum of more than eighteen cents had occurred that day, the groom might be accorded a whole sentence to himself. If his family was exceptionally prominent he might even get a compound sentence and have his middle name spelled correctly. The case of William Pettus springs to mind. Bill was nipped by a filly in the spring of 1944 and, while he was hardly what you would call notorious, I have always felt he deserved more than "the groom is in the Army Air Corps and shot down nine Messerschmitts last month."

One crisis arose immediately. Sally's mother had written me an affectionate note, telling me in so many words that she had no idea what I saw in her elder daughter, and that she had raised Weyman's wages, and then plunging headlong into the subject of engraved invitations. My full title, it developed, was "Lieutenant (junior grade) Donald Robert Morris, United States Navy," and the engraver claimed that this was altogether too long. Would there be any objection to his leaving out the "(junior grade)"? I wrote back and pointed out that this would constitute an entirely unwarranted promotion and that "United States Navy" was a model of brevity compared to the "Royal New Zealand Volunteer Auxiliary Naval Air Force Reserve (Retired)" with which one lady of our acquaintance had to cope. My mother recalled another friend who had addressed over three hundred announcements on her son's behalf when he was promoted by an unthinking Army two weeks before the wedding. His mother-in-law insisted on a new plate and she had to do the whole damn list over.

A number of commercial organizations were also getting into the act. The first ones to take cognizance of the coming festivities were the loan companies. No less than eight rallied around, with offers of assistance that ranged from a man-to-man "Do you need cash?" to a more studied effort beginning "Now, more than ever before . . ." Three of these companies hung on like grim death, bombarding me with ever more attractive offers to fill my pockets with silver and gold, even after the ceremony. Keep trying, boys. You never can tell.

Next came a letter from Sally outlining the stand the sovereign state of North Carolina was taking. Since I only planned to arrive in Little Hominy the evening before the wedding, there would be no opportunity for a blood test on home grounds. North Carolina was not taking any chances with sailors and agreed to accept a test administered by the Navy only after Sally's mother called the Governor and brought up the hoof marks in the library again. I promised to get a test while we were in Greenland.

I went out for a sandwich and a cup of coffee (our kitchen looked as if it would be out of action for some time to come) and when I got back I was pinned to the wall by the question, What was Sally's mother going to wear? I had given remarkably little thought to this question, but it turned out that not only weddings but inter-family relations are usually made or marred right there. Weddings are almost entirely a matter of female clothing. Until I witnessed it myself, I had no idea that one pink slipper could sustain an animated telephone conversation for twenty-seven and one-half minutes, and then only giving way to the subject of stockings, nor that a snippet of some unidentified bluish material, measuring one eighth by one sixteenth of an inch, could throw an entire cultivated household into confusion. The morsel involved had been clipped from the hem of the dress my future sister-in-law intended to wear and for some reason totally excluded the possibility of the dress my mother hoped to wear and was only partially compatible with my aunt's hat. It also ruled out my father's necktie. All these articles were hastily exchanged, although the matter of Father's necktie was not settled until he swore that if he did attend—an event that was growing more and more unlikely—it would be in a bright purple necktie and with no shirt.

The last time I had seen *male* attire cause such an uproar was two years back, when I had spent a week's leave with Schuyler. His entire family had been invited to a masquerade, and Schuyler's grandfather, who had lost a leg at San Juan Hill, insisted on going as a pirate. Schuyler dutifully went out and hired a pirate suit, but the afternoon of the ball the old boy decided he didn't want to go as a pirate after all; he wanted to go as a gypsy. A big argument started, which was only stopped when Schuyler flatly stated that if there was one more word on the subject he would ram his crutch up his rear end, paint him red and send him as a candied apple.

The Navy's dress white uniform was designed around 1880 and has undergone no appreciable change since then. A brand-new set of whites cost $15.50, with the buttons $1.00 extra, both items tax-deductible. I couldn't see what the fuss was all about.

My father, in a rash moment, asked what he could do to help. Nobody was paying much attention to him either, except to snatch at his checkbook every now and again. Mother immediately set him to addressing envelopes. To save time she had offered to address and mail invitations to her part of the guest list, and she had already purchased the envelopes. This turned out to be a pitfall of almost bottomless proportions, and Father wound up not speaking to any of us until two days before the ceremony.

The first problem was the list. I turned in one with twenty-eight names. My parents countered with three hundred and sixteen names, only seven of which appeared on my list. It included two hundred and eight people I had never heard of and the Secretary of the Navy. After two furious hours I got eight names struck off the list, including the Secretary's, but I think Mother sneaked him one anyway.

Father started in on the envelopes with the list standing at three hundred and twenty-nine names. After forty-two envelopes had been finished, it was pointed out to him that the addresses had to be handwritten. He started over again, still in cheerful spirits, and at sixty-seven wandered out to ask why the envelopes seemed to be two different sizes. It was then explained that each invitation required two envelopes and that only the names went on the inner one. Of the sixty-seven finished envelopes, sixty-three were inner envelopes with addresses and had to be discarded. The third time he did better, only starting addresses on about every fifth inner envelope. At two in the morning he staggered out in triumph with the entire col-

lection, addressed and stamped. Mother took one look and
told him that under no circumstances would the invitations
go out with return addresses. It was at this point that
Father stopped speaking to us. Mother had to reorder envelopes and the entire process consumed four days and
one thousand thirty-eight envelopes, of which the last few
score were addressed in green ink in a barely decipherable
scrawl. Bits of envelopes turned up all over the apartment
for months.

We had very little trouble with the guests. Everybody
wanted to come, but after a few minutes of describing how
to get to Little Hominy, enthusiasm cooled rapidly.

The one person I was bound to have at my wedding was
my oldest friend, Jimmy. Jimmy had gone to West Point
and was now a captain in the Air Force. He hadn't shot
down nine Messerschmitts, but he *had* shot down a MIG,
and on the Fourth of July at that. *Time* carried his picture,
standing on the wing of his Saber jet, helmet in crooked
elbow, staring quizzically off into space. I hadn't seen him
for some time and didn't even know exactly where he was
stationed. Calling the Pentagon to find out and getting
through to him in California was considerably less strain
than calling Little Hominy.

"Wedding? . . . You! . . . My God! . . . Sure, sure . . . I'll
get there. Wouldn't miss it for worlds. . . . Where the hell is
it? . . . Little Hominy? . . . You're kidding. . . . Has it got an
airstrip? . . . It does, huh? . . . Never mind the details, I'll
find out from the Air Force. . . . *Sure* we got 'em all listed. . . .

Yeah, even Little Hominy. . . . Four o'clock, huh? Let's see.
I've got to be in Morocco the next morning, but as long as
I hit New York by seven . . . Look, have someone meet me
at the field at fifteen-thirty hours sharp. . . . Yeah, yeah,
shouldn't take over an hour, should it? . . . Right, right. . . .
So long, kid."

Jimmy was coming.

When I got back aboard the ship on the morning we were
to leave, the wedding receded into the background and the
Navy took over again. The ship was all set for the trip,
except for the fact that El Toro was still with us. No one
in New York seemed to want a goat, either.

Schuyler had gotten himself on a quiz program and had
won a movie camera and a tripod. The equipment wakened
some long-dormant creative chord in his soul and he had
already shot two pictures about New York, one entirely
in subways, and was planning a long epic about polar ex-
ploration as soon as we got to Greenland.

Schuyler had also visited his anthropology professor at
Columbia to see what he could do about an Italian-Chicka-
saw dictionary. The anthropologist had not been much
help. An assistant had finally unearthed from the archives
a handwritten master's thesis by a Bulgarian on Apache
verb forms. The manuscript was in Bulgarian and was
dated 1894. Schuyler didn't see where this was going to be
any help at all, until he was presented with a Bulgarian-
Italian dictionary and a Chickasaw-Apache dictionary
written by a Spanish missionary in 1838. The anthropolo-

gist told him he could probably work something up out of all that material, and if we met any Smith Sound Eskimos would we please try to get some tape recordings, especially of diphthongs. Schuyler said we'd try.

The trip to Thule took almost three weeks and was fun. We were steaming by ourselves, which always helped, because we didn't have to keep station on another ship. Navigation was a snap until we transited the Straits of Belle Isle and entered Davis Straits. The Straits of Belle Isle seemed quite straightforward, but Captain O'Gara was a bit put out by the geographical nomenclature that had been accumulating there in the course of the centuries. Shipwreck Point gave way to Cannibal Cove, and Deadman's Beach led to Skull Rock.

Navigation, however, didn't get really hairy until we worked our way well up the western coast of Greenland. As long as a navigator has a good chart and sees stars once in a while he is a fairly happy man. Charts with lots of soundings may show shoal water, but at least they indicate that someone has been there before, and usually quite recently. Certain types of entries, however, are not calculated to inspire confidence in a navigator's breast, and the upper reaches of Baffin Bay fairly crawl with remarks like "Breakers reported by HMS *Weaseltail* in 1876." We were bushwhacking, which means feeling your way from point to point along the coast, a process that again depends on an accurate chart. A long dotted line, with gaps, labeled

"Based on dog-sled survey conducted in 1911," is not an acceptable substitute.

Dead reckoning is all very well, and piloting can be very enjoyable when you have something like the Empire State Building or Mount Fujiyama to take bearings on, but in Greenland there are certain disadvantages. The scenery in Greenland consists exclusively of glaciers, and the front, or business end, of a glacier is apt to look exactly like a surprising number of other glaciers, and all the glaciers in Greenland can pass for each other in any kind of light.

By the time we suspected we might just possibly be lost, the sun started to stay up permanently and we were far enough north for both the magnetic and the gyro compasses to be affected. All the modern electronic aids to navigation are no substitute for a good three-star celestial fix, and with no stars available the modern navigator feels a sudden sympathy for the Queen of Sheba's sailors groping hopefully along the coast of Punt.

We finally reduced the area the ship was probably in to a square two hundred miles on a side, using the combined navigational skills of all hands, including Chief Popper, who was an Eagle Scout and claimed to know more about glaciers than the rest of us. He had a merit badge in them, or something. It got a little colder, which was just as well, because on the bridge we had to wear the new foul-weather gear issued in New York.

The new outfits started with long johns and worked their

way up through bizarre layers of odd cut and odder textiles to a final hooded parka, firmly strapped and zippered over everything that went below. There was a face mask with goggles and buttoned flaps for the mouth and nose, and boots that laced, zipped and belted over descending legs of subsidiary layers. I held the ship's record for answering a call of nature from a fully buttoned condition—four minutes and eighteen seconds. Until the trouble with the cigarette, I felt myself one with Peary.

The cigarette incident occurred on the morning I reached the bridge and suddenly realized that both tobacco and lighter were in my shirt pocket, about seven stops down the line. It was the first really cold day, and the ship was headed into the teeth of a strong, moist breeze. I pulled off the heavy outer mittens and the gloves, unbuttoned the mouth flap, and held the mittens and gloves in my teeth. Then I pushed aside my slung binoculars, unbelted, unbuttoned and unzipped the parka, and unzipped the windbreaker. I undid the front of the overalls, lowered them far enough to get at the bottom edge of my sweater, raised that and unbuttoned the vest, undid my shirt pocket, got the cigarettes out, put them on the gyro repeater, buttoned my shirt pocket and vest, pulled down the sweater, pulled up the overalls and fastened them, zipped up the windbreaker, zipped, buttoned and belted the parka, and replaced the gloves, mittens, face mask, parka hood, and binoculars.

Then I remembered my lighter.

By the time I got the lighter out I needed the cigarette badly. I unbuttoned the mouth flap, pushed a cigarette through, and poked until I found my mouth. I tried to light it, but because of the goggles and the nose flap I couldn't see the end of the cigarette and burned my nose. Since the nose was cold to begin with, I didn't realize it was burning until the process was well underway. I pushed the hood back, identified my nose and the end of the cigarette,

pinched the former gently, and lit the latter. Then I replaced the goggles and hood.

When I started to exhale, the smoke caught inside the
face mask and I started to cough. I reached up to pull the
cigarette out, but what with the mittens and all it caught
inside the mouth flap and slipped down to my chin. I
tried to pull the face mask off, but the goggles and the
parka hood and the binocular strap were all in the way.
I pulled off the gloves and mittens again, pushed the parka
hood back, pulled off my watch cap and started to work on
the straps at the back of my head. I couldn't tell the binocular strap from the goggle strap from the face mask strap,
and my hands were getting cold.

While I was fumbling with the straps I suddenly realized
that something (it later turned out to be the turtleneck
sweater) was on fire. I started to yell, but since I was still
coughing and had a number of things in my mouth, no one
understood me. It was particularly muffled over the voice
tube, and the helmsman thought I said "Right Full Rudder" and he put the helm over. The man at the engine-order
telegraph thought he heard "All Back Full" and made it so.
The quartermaster thought I said "Meyer," who was on
watch in the engineroom, and sent for him. The messenger
thought it was "Fire," which was correct, but everybody
told him he was crazy. He got into an argument and they
finally compromised on sounding General Quarters. When
the Captain got to the pilothouse, the messenger insisted
there was a fire somewhere, so the Captain sounded the

fire alarm too. All stations were manned and everybody looked for the fire but nobody could find one.

The Captain then climbed up to the conning tower and saw me thrashing around in a dense cloud of smoke near the voice tubes. I had gotten partially out of the parka, which had slipped down around my elbows and was hampering me considerably. The Captain ran over and at once decided that all the smoke was coming out of the new voice tube from the engine room, so he sent the fire party down there. Murdoch was sitting at the log-room desk bringing his logs up to date when the fire party burst in and started to spray him with chemical fog.

By this time I had finally gotten some of the gear out of my mouth and I started to yell for help. One of the quartermasters finally spotted the difficulty and put the fire out with a cup of coffee. I had to be led below and unpacked. It took quite some time for the excitement to die down.

Late that evening we ran into fog. Even the fog up here was different; dense, opaque patches alternated with clear areas. Fog always caused more trouble on our ship than on other ships. The LSTs had originally been designed for very short voyages, and much of the gear regarded as standard equipment on other ships had been tacked on to us more or less as an afterthought. The Captain's sea cabin, for example, which was right under the conning tower, faced aft on the signal deck, and the fog horn, attached to the mainmast right aft of the sea cabin, practically blew the paint off the sea-cabin door when it sounded. Between the sea cabin and the mainmast rested Secondary Conn, a large metal binnacle with the spare magnetic compass, flanked by the iron spheres known as the navigator's balls.

The sea cabin, besides the cot the Captain used underway, also contained spare signal flags and tarpaulins. Since the compartment was unheated, the skipper, when he tried to sleep in it, would cover himself with all the blankets and tarps and signal flags he could find. It was, consequently, a little hard to see whether or not he was actually in it, and you had to poke around a bit to make sure. If the wind blew in on the cot, he would sometimes curl up on deck in the opposite corner, which made it even harder to see if he was there or not.

The fog horn was used not only for fog but also to make the whistle signals required by the Rules of the Road. If the skipper wasn't on the bridge, it was mandatory to get his permission before starting fog signals. If he was below and heard a blast, he had no way of telling if it was a sudden emergency requiring his immediate presence on the bridge or a fog bank the Officer of the Deck could handle by himself, with the aid of the radar.

The Captain had already turned in for the night when we encountered the first fog patch. The chances of meeting a ship in it were pretty slim, since the radar scope showed a clear sea for miles around and there were practically no other ships this far north anyway. Even so, fog signals were called for, and Schuyler, who had the deck, sent the messenger to find Captain O'Gara. The messenger finally came back and said he couldn't find him. Schuyler asked the messenger if he had checked the sea cabin, and the messenger, who was new and didn't know about O'Gara sometimes sleeping on deck, said yes.

This wasn't too unusual, because the skipper might be in the head or visiting in crew's quarters or inspecting an icebox, but Schuyler got worried, because the fog was pretty thick by then, and he started sounding fog signals anyway.

The first blast lifted O'Gara right off the deck of the sea cabin, tarpaulins and all. Since it had been perfectly clear, with no hint of fog, when he turned in, he of course as-

sumed we were in the jaws of a collision, and when he hit the deck he was running. He came charging out of the sea cabin, crashed head-on into the starboard navigator's ball, and laid himself out cold.

The fog patch lifted, and Schuyler, glancing down from the conning tower, saw the skipper lying peacefully on the signal deck, still pretty well covered with tarpaulins and signal flags. Schuyler was outraged.

"Look at that!" he yelled at the messenger. "You could have stepped on him when you were looking in the sea cabin!"

The messenger insisted that he hadn't been sleeping on the deck when he, the messenger, was down there, and while they were arguing the Captain pulled himself groggily to his feet, climbed up to the conning tower and, not seeing any fog, decided it was still a case of "in extremis" and sounded General Quarters. This one took quite a while to settle, because the skipper was really pretty groggy and before he was straightened out we were back in a fog patch. The skipper finally turned in again, after tying a stout cord to his ankle and telling Schuyler to yank once for fog, twice for other ships, before sounding the whistle again. He also took two tarpaulins and padded the navigator's balls.

We reached Thule with no further mishaps. The Air Force sent out helicopters to look for us and guide us into the bay, and we dislodged a small iceberg from our assigned berth and dropped the hook.

Vlasser went in after the mail and Schuyler went with him to see if anybody in Greenland wanted a goat, as a curio, and whether he could round up some Eskimos for his epic.

We looked around us. If any real estate in the world was less prepossessing than Vieques, this was it. Vegetation was nonexistent, and the land rose in ice-bound rocky ledges to the high interior. The Air Force had located what seemed to be the only flat area on the entire island and set up shop there.

I was in the ship's office when Schuyler and Vlasser returned. Schuyler reported that goats were, if anything, in less demand in Greenland than anywhere else, and that the nearest Eskimo village was strictly out of bounds for all hands.

I started for my cabin and passed Vlasser in the passageway. He gave me a look of disgust.

"What're ya trying to do, kill me, sir?"

I looked into my cabin. The desk was covered with a sort of drifted snow effect.

"For me?" I asked brightly.

"Every goddam one. Two hunnert twenny-eight."

I sat down delightedly. I had never been so popular before. Some five hours later, as I clawed my way out of the discarded envelopes, I began to have an inkling of what lay ahead.

The agitation that had prevailed when I passed through New York was apparently as nothing to what must be going on there by now. The word had gotten around, and new problems were cropping up.

I already had a letter from Sally's mother, and I had heard about a sister, but I was totally unprepared for the hordes of aunts, uncles, cousins and friends who now disclosed themselves. I was also unprepared for their attitude. Everybody kept rubbing in that I was undoubtedly "the luckiest man on earth." I had always thought this was a modest form of self-depreciation reserved for the use of the groom himself, and its constant reiteration by a horde of strangers soon had me feeling that the engagement was a sheer fluke; I had caught Sally in an unguarded moment and taken advantage of her. The fact that this was basically true didn't help my feelings at all.

Two of Sally's childhood friends sent snapshots which, they claimed, I was now entitled to. In one, Sally, at the age of ten, peered over a watermelon rind to reveal pigtails and no front teeth. In the other, she was costumed as the Sandman in *Hansel and Gretel* and revealed nothing at all except for two long, spindly shanks. I sent these on to New York to help fill what was obviously an insatiable appetite for photographic material of any description.

There was also a certain redundancy of Dudleys. One Dudley Stubblefield had apparently distinguished himself at the Battle of Little Hominy. As far as I could make out, he seemed to be responsible for the hoof marks getting as far as the library, and no subsequent generation was regarded as complete without at least one Dudley. There were now four cousins, somebody's brother and an aunt all named Dudley. There was even a Dudley Dudley. Some of them were not speaking to other Dudleys, and all resented being mistaken for any other Dudley, particularly the Cousin Dudley who lived in Charleston.

Various chapters of the United Daughters of the Battle of Little Hominy wrote to ask if I could show sufficient documentation to include myself on their rolls, in which case any female children of Sally's and mine would automatically become eligible not only for the St. Cecilia Ball but also for the annual "Maid of Cotton" award. I did have a great-uncle who served in a Louisiana infantry regiment. He had been a New York life-insurance salesman who had been in New Orleans when the war broke out and who had enlisted to clinch a sale to the Colonel of the regiment, but he had deserted the instant the ink was dry on the policy, and the only documentation we had left was a gaudy poster offering $250 for his recapture. This turned out to be unacceptable, even though I pointed out that the man could hardly have deserted if he hadn't enlisted in the first place, and besides, the Colonel had never paid any of the premiums.

A surprising number of letters from total strangers asked me what we would like for a wedding present. The last time anyone offered to buy me something was shortly before my seventh birthday, and I was sadly out of practice. No sound body of doctrine exists on this subject, and it is an important one. New households the nation over are forever blighted by the presence of ceramic parakeets four feet high, cigarette lighters cunningly disguised to look like clipper ships, limed-oak plaques with "God Bless Our Mortgaged Home" engraved on them in Gothic letters, and other examples of what may happen if Aunt Matilda is not headed off in time.

In our case, foresight was lacking. We now own four umbrella stands just because I got sarcastic in the last dreadful week, and our collection of cocktail shakers includes every known building material except cinder block. Many people called my parents and asked what Sally *really* wanted. My parents called Sally to ask, and she proved something less than helpful.

"Anything so long as it's not 'His' and 'Hers' towels" was all they could get out of her.

This narrowed the field somewhat, but not enough. We were going to Naples and wanted to travel light, and, as I pointed out to my parents, nothing is as light as a check. Eventually we wound up with four sets of "His" and "Hers" towels, including one "He" and "She" variation.

Once the gifts started to arrive a certain amount of fast footwork was necessary. We got twenty-four identical steak knives from three separate sources. We decided that if twenty-four people ever came to dinner we weren't going to be serving anything they couldn't eat with a spoon, so twelve knives went back and somehow turned into a cocktail dress for Sally.

"I can wear it when we serve steak," she explained.

One gift shop in New York was approached by no less than fourteen relatives and friends, and within four working days managed to unload a dozen solid-silver trays. Sally visited this establishment later to return ten of them and discovered that all twelve had been sold by the same sales clerk.

The newspaper clippings forwarded to me varied; Sally got the full treatment, although the paper she worked for referred to her throughout the engagement announcement as "Mrs." Two papers didn't mention me at all, one left off my last name, and another reported I was about to enter the Coast Guard.

The Little Hominy *Weekly Skillet* ("Everything Piping Hot") sent a correspondent all the way to Norfolk to get an exclusive. I don't know whom he interviewed there, but he came back to Little Hominy under the impression that Sally was going to marry an Indian named Sneaking Beagle Morrow. It caused a big uproar among the Dudleys, and Sally's mother had to call the Governor again.

Then a columnist in Los Angeles got a copy of the *Weekly Skillet* and confused Sneaking Beagle with a prominent local dope smuggler named Sneaky Peter Marveles. This would have been fairly easy to do, since the *Weekly Skillet* makes its own newsprint and ink and the result leaves something to be desired, but unfortunately my New York address was brilliantly legible and correctly reported by the Los Angeles man.

Three armed agents of an unidentified organization

visited my mother, searched the apartment, and insisted on hiding in the clothes closet opposite the front door. They claimed Sneaky Peter was due any moment and refused to let Mother go out or use the telephone. When Father got home from the office and went to hang up his hat they set him back no end. Around ten o'clock that evening Mother brought them some coffee. They were still there in the morning, a little wilted, and Mother insisted that they leave, because she was expecting some people for lunch. They finally got out of the closet, but they took turns loitering around the apartment-house lobby for months.

Then I heard from the jewelers. No ring. The factory was closed for the summer. Nobody should get married before the first of June, anyway. I telegraphed the branch office in Annapolis and the East Coast office in Hoboken and they both said, Try the factory. Then Dad offered to help. He was still refusing to have anything to do with the postal system, but he offered to call a friend in Detroit who played golf with the department-store buyer of a local store owned by a man who was a close friend of the ex-vice president of the local chapter of the National Jewelers' Association. This sounded a little tenuous, but I was clutching at straws.

About there the mail petered out, and I was left sitting in Greenland making little red marks on a calendar. I was acting, O'Gara told me, just like a Brown Bagger.

CHAPTER 9

THE third day in Greenland we beached the ship, unloaded all our gear, loaded the equipment we were to take
back, and got ready to leave. El Toro came down to the
ramp to have a look at Greenland, and we all held our
breath, but he decided it wasn't a nickel's worth of im-
provement over Vieques and refused to get off. I really
couldn't blame him much.

Then I suddenly remembered the blood test I had promised the state of North Carolina and hunted out the Air
Force dispensary.

"I want a blood test, please," I told the duty doctor.

The duty doctor looked up from his magazine. "What for?" he asked suspiciously.

"I have to have one," I answered truthfully. Everybody knew that.

"You wait right here," the doctor said. He put down his magazine and left the room. In about ten minutes he was back with a colonel.

"This the one?" he asked.

"Yes, sir. Navy type. Just up here for a few days."

"Young man," the Colonel started, "you should be ashamed of yourself."

I looked startled.

"Thoroughly ashamed," the Colonel continued. "For years our relations with the indigenous population have been cordial and polite. We treat them with the dignity and respect their ancient and noble culture deserves. Then you come along. In addition to the grave personal risks you have obviously run, you have set Eskimo-American relations back for years."

A light dawned.

"Colonel," I broke in, "you've got it all wrong. I just want to get married."

It slowed the Colonel down, but it didn't really stop him.

"Married! Look, I don't know the girl, but you're making a hell of a mistake. The paperwork takes months, and we have to clear it with Copenhagen. Have you ever considered how hard walrus meat is to come by in most American cities?"

I finally got the Colonel's mind off Eskimos, but I had to go back to the ship to get Sally's last letter before I got the blood test. The duty doctor said he'd mail the results back to Little Hominy. I printed the address very clearly, and asked him please to make it special delivery.

The trip home seemed to fly. For once we had a tail wind, and all the bearings behaved themselves. After Belle Isle Straits we shed the new foul-weather clothing and wrote a long report to the Development people. They replied we had everything on in the wrong order except the parkas, and would we please check the markings on the face mask to see if they had "Mark VII Mod 4a" in them, because from our description they sounded like part of the new gas mask.

We were due in Norfolk just before noon Friday, and I spent most of the last week working over the Leave and Liberty list. For once, however, I slipped up.

The Navy has wisely and rightly set up a series of hard and fast rules governing the exact conditions under which a man may leave a ship. One of the hardest battles an Executive Officer must face is the constant encroachment on these rules, a struggle waged ceaselessly with varying degrees of success by every man in the crew.

Since leave has to start sometime, the Navy has decided that morning quarters is as good a time as any. If a man's leave starts at eight o'clock Monday morning, however, there is no earthly reason he can see why he can't shove off after work on Friday, provided he rates liberty over the weekend. This is perfectly all right with the Executive Officer, provided the man changes his leave chit to Friday, in which case he can go at quarters on Friday morning. This the man does *not* want to do, since it means paying out three more days of his accumulated leave credit. If he is forced to change it to Friday, he can't see why he shouldn't leave after working hours on *Thursday*. Sure, says the Exec, always a good schnuck, just change the chit to Thursday and . . . You can see what he's up against. Pick any ship in the Navy, pop into the Exec's stateroom, and the chances are three out of five you will find him standing in front of his mirror practicing how to say "No" with the proper blend of benevolence, finality and good leadership. Once he has mastered this trick he is ready for what are known as "higher duties"—i.e., Captain, when he can tell people "See the Exec" instead of having to say "No" himself.

On our ship all Special Requests had to be in writing and had to be approved by the Division Officers first. This was intended to screen the requests, but since no Division Officer in his right mind would turn one of his own men down, they always sent *all* the requests on to the Executive Officer, who was supposed to be the ship's official son of a bitch anyway. Over the last year and a half I had encountered the Special Request chit in its every conceivable form and variation and I prided myself on my ability to spot the really deserving cases among all the obvious sporting efforts.

When Lester Wallace, therefore, presented a chit asking to be let off on Saturday because he could get a ride that would take him just two blocks from his home in Brattleboro, thus saving a day and a half of his leave, I said sure and approved it. Later in the day both Victor Blue and Buddy Watkins presented similar chits, Blue claiming he had a chance for a ride right into South Adams and Watkins stating that he had one all the way to Portland. I also approved these chits.

Twenty minutes later Vlasser brought a Special Request in. He wanted off Saturday, the chit said, because he had to drive Wallace, Blue and Watkins up to New England.

I worked over this one for an hour, but it looked foolproof. I called Vlasser back and said I'd approve his chit provided he took El Toro all the way to Portland and left him there. Vlasser hedged, claiming all he had was a Model-A roadster and that someone was going to have to ride in the rumble seat as it was. I was adamant. No goat, no chit. He finally left to cut cards for the rumble seat. Watkins lost.

We came through the Capes early Friday morning, steamed up Thimble Shoals Channel, and asked for pier space. We might just as well have saved our breaths. Carriers, cruisers, battleships and transports were all in for the weekend, and LSTs were taking their chances in South How anchorage, along with other naval oddments. From there we could make our liberty in small craft.

This was only to be expected, but it was still a blow. All small craft made the same Fleet Landing, and Fleet Landing around noon on weekends was not a particularly pleasant place to spend much time. It serviced over fifty naval vessels and the area by the landing floats was always jammed with a tremendous crowd of sailors and officers waiting for their ship's boats to come and get them. By themselves, they would have caused confusion enough, but they were vastly outnumbered by a mass of women and children who might have been waiting for some luckless bastard for as much as five hours. To dependents, all small craft and most sailors look alike, and over the shrieks of mistaken recognition rose the howls of lost children and the strident demands for ice cream, boat rides or sailor hats of those whose parents had not yet managed to lose them. There was always a terrifying proportion of what the Navy refers to in its official literature as "gravid dependent females" among those present, and even Jack the Stitcher quailed when he was assigned the day's duty at the Fleet Landing. Sally later said it was all very like the ballad of Sir Patrick Spens—"lang, lang will their ladies sit, with their fans unto their hands"—and why hadn't we gone to Charleston or Beaufort where there were nice hotels?

She had written me that her mother and Sugar Plum were both coming to Norfolk with her to meet the ship and bring me back to Little Hominy. The wedding was to be Saturday; Sally said she needed to get away from the preparations and that her mother was coming in order to get to know me before the actual ceremony. Sugar Plum was traveling with them by popular demand—he had come upon a brand-new source for his favorite perfume, *l'essence des poissons morts depuis longtemps*—and it was hoped that the ride would air him out before the guests started to arrive.

We dropped the hook at noon and the LCVP started in for Fleet Landing with the first of the liberty party and two cases of what the Stitcher insisted were poison ivy.

Shrieking Eagle was coxswain. I instructed the Stitcher that if he saw two ladies with red hair and a large white dog with black spots, to avoid the dog at all costs and tell either one of the ladies I would be along shortly.

When the LCVP got back I had the logs signed and the monthly reports up and the office cleaned out. The Captain wished me a happy wedding day and handed me a leave chit for eight days. I climbed down to the LCVP and Shrieking Eagle backed clear and headed for the landing. The Quarterdeck Watch wished me good luck, and the Captain waved. A lump came into my throat. When I saw the ship again I would be *married*.

Even Shrieking Eagle noticed my condition and patted me on the shoulder. He also mumbled something in Chickasaw, of which I caught only the word for "tent."

We pulled into the landing and Shrieking Eagle cut the engine. The Bow Hook jumped out and snubbed his line and Shrieking Eagle smiled up at the Shore Patrolman on the float as I stepped out. The Shore Patrolman stared at him vacantly for a moment and then recognition and horror dawned slowly in his eyes.

"He's back!" he shouted, stumbling as he turned toward the control shack. "Garfield's back!"

Over the noise of the crowd I heard a distant cry of pain. The Chief of the Patrol burst out of a side door, jumped into a police car and started for town with the siren screaming. Other Patrolmen, white-faced, poured out and crowded toward the waterfront to see. Shrieking Eagle pared his calluses and ignored them. I started up the float.

At the head of the float there was a commotion behind a knot of sailors and suddenly Sugar Plum struck me full in the chest. He seemed glad to see me, but it was always hard to tell exactly what he had on his mind. I got up cautiously and spotted Sally close behind.

"Darling!" I croaked, and kissed her. Sugar Plum put a paw between my shoulders and I fell down again, this time on top of Sally. I still had my mind on kissing, and saw no reason to stop, and there were approving murmurs from all the sailors, which were interrupted by a discreet cough. I looked over my shoulder and discovered that an attractive lady with blue eyes was regarding me critically. The sailors had fallen respectfully back to give us all plenty of room.

"I would like you," Sally said with a great deal of aplomb, "to meet my mother."

The trip down to Little Hominy was not soothing. I was still jumpy and Sally was obviously in for a sequestered interrogation on the exact circumstances under which we became engaged. Vlasser had put my mail in the back of the car, and Sugar Plum was sorting it industriously. Every now and again, usually on blind curves, he would bring

the remnants of a particularly interesting letter to me in
his jaws, shoving insistently against the back of my neck
to attract attention.

By South Hill we were all friends again, and the wedding
plans were beating around my ears. In order to purchase
more than the six bottles of champagne that was all the
liquor laws of North Carolina would allow to a customer,
Bustard's Roost had had to be licensed as a cabaret, alienat-
ing a round dozen Dudleys and gladdening Weyman's
heart. Cousin Bob was coming all the way from Houston to
marry us, and the Louisiana Historical Association had
found the enlistment papers and it was all right for the
St. Cecilia Ball. Sally's mother had warned the florist that
if there were ants all over the bride's bouquet the way
there had been at her niece Tanya Rene's wedding she
would not pay the bill, since Tanya Rene had scratched
not only all through the ceremony but also all the way to
Pawley's Island. And there was to be a big tent on the lawn
in case it rained during the reception and . . .

A small bell tinkled faintly in my muffled consciousness
and then clanged in a great peal. We were rounding a
curve and I almost left the highway.

"Tent. A tent? What tent?"

"It belongs to the United Daughters of the Battle of
Little Hominy. Cousin Bob says he's going to hold a revival meeting in it immediately after the ceremony, and
Tanya Rene says she's going to *wear* it *at* the reception, if
she can hold the baby back that long. And that nice sailor

from your ship, offering to put it up and all. Why didn't you come in the first boat, like he did?"

"You asked Shrieking Eagle to the wedding? Good God, woman, do you realize what you did?"

"Do you want one of us to drive, dear? You almost hit that 'Stop' sign. He was terribly nice. He likes you. He says you speak Chickasaw with a Shoshone accent."

"You *can't* ask Shrieking Eagle to the wedding. Lie down, Sugar Plum. The nearest sheriff is ten miles away."

"Not with an election coming up and all his constituents gathered under one roof. *Please* watch the road, dear."

It seemed to me that there were a lot of people at Bustard's Roost already, including Sally's sister Daphne, who took a soothing maternal attitude toward both of us. Like Schuyler, she was an anthropology major, and it would have been just as hard to tell. The general condition of the house reminded me a little of New York, except that the house was bigger and the traffic a little more scientifically controlled. Two small children were planted on the kitchen steps with a machine that shaved ice which they then packed away in the cellar. A whole squad of volunteers was maneuvering with potted palms in the parlor, which looked like Birnam Wood. Sally and her mother disappeared at once; no one paid me the slightest attention and I looked desperately for Weyman. I finally found him under the scuppernong arbor, honing ham knives, and he cut me in.

"County Medical Officer been here twicet today; he

wants that blood test. Your folks telegraphed from New York; they're all set to get here in the morning. Said it was the first time the Pennsylvania Station ever sold a ticket to Lye, and the *Times* wanted to send a man to do a story. I think your mother headed him off. Mr. Dudley in Charleston wrote you a letter. Hasn't written anybody up here since Woodrow Wilson was elected. You in, sir. You can relax."

It was late, but I wanted to call New York and check with my parents about meeting them in the morning. All they had to do was get to Lye; I didn't want them to try to make Little Hominy by themselves. It was my first attempt at telephoning *out* of Little Hominy.

The Hominy operator sounded glad to hear me again. She asked me how Greenland had been and then got through to Lye, via Big Hominy. Lye was apparently a staging area for telephonic invasions of the North.

"Noo Yawk? This is Little Hominy."

"Hello? Hello?"

"Little Hominy, that is."

"Hello! New York here!"

"That's right. This is Little Hominy. I'm a-calling you."

"Who? Operator! Operator! I'm talking to Lye, Virginia."

"Not now, you ain't, honey. They put you through to Little Hominy. Say, was it you I talked to when the Watts boy called up on V-J night?" She momentarily lowered her voice in a conversational aside to me. "From Payris, France."

"What number are you calling? What is *your* number, Operator?"

"This is Hallie Burke. I don't have a number because there's nobody here but me. You all got a Rhinelander up there, honey?"

When we finally got through, my parents were relieved to hear from me. I had long ago given up trying to explain exactly where Sally lived, and they were under the impression that I was calling from Greenland. I had once called New York from Pearl Harbor on New Year's Eve and Mother somehow got the idea I was calling from Grand Central Station. She kept telling me to wait; she'd be right down to get me. This time the New York operator was frankly dubious about the call and refused to get off the line. In a few minutes Mother had convinced both the New York and the Lye operators that I *was* calling from Greenland, and neither the Little Hominy operator nor I was able to straighten anybody out. I finally put Sally on and Mother immediately thought we had eloped and gone to Greenland for our honeymoon and started to cry.

I didn't want to hang up until I was sure Mother understood she was to be on the train that got into Lye at nine-thirty the next morning and I kept repeating the name of the train. The New York supervisor listened for a while, and then an operator from Greenfield, Missouri, came on the line and asked us what number we wanted. I was trying to deal with her when a new voice popped up. This turned out to be a teacher at the Greenacres Elementary

School in Hartsdale, New York, and unfortunately her name was Lydia Holiday. At this point the New York operator started to cry, and I think Mother hung up, so I did too.

I asked for a drink, and Sally mixed me one.

"Never mind," she said. "They never send a bill anyway."

I was just relaxing when the telephone rang. It was Hallie Burke.

"You shouldn't have been so short with her, honey," she said. "That Noo Yawk girl is plumb crazy, and her supervisor says just as soon as she finds out where Little Hominy *is*, she's comin' down and personally rip out every instrument in the county. See you all tomorrow."

Sally brought over the scraps of mail left over from Sugar Plum's attentions and we sorted them out. As far as we could tell, there was nothing of any importance, except that the ring was not going to arrive in time. I decided it wasn't worth calling my parents again to tell them to bring a ring—any ring—down, and Sally said Cousin Bob claimed he once had to marry a couple in a hurry and had used a curtain ring, and we would certainly manage.

Then the County Medical Officer called again and asked for the blood test. We went through the whole pile of paper once more, but couldn't find anything that even faintly resembled it.

"Any time before the ceremony, boy." There was a threatening pause. "Just so long as I get it."

Shortly before midnight a pickup truck pulled into the

front yard, and Schuyler got out. The back of the truck was filled with movie gear.

"Had to rent it all in Norfolk," he explained after he opened the back. "But what a script! *The Girl Gunner of the Merrimac!*"

"How," I asked, "did you get the hell here? In the dark yet?"

"Easy, kid. No sweat. The old man give us two days' leave."

There was a convulsive upheaval in the back of the truck, while light stands and sound equipment and a tripod slithered to the ground. A dark figure rose and stretched.

"Shrieking Eagle, here," Schuyler said, "told me when to turn."

I went in to get another drink. While I was pouring it, Schuyler came in the front door, followed by Shrieking Eagle. Sugar Plum danced delightedly around both of them. Then El Toro stuck his head in, saw Sugar Plum, bleated, and scampered up stairs.

Carefully I poured the drink back and sat down.

"El Toro. I distinctly saw El Toro. He's in Portland. How the hell did *he* get here?"

Schuyler pried my fingers from around his elbow.

"Wedding present from the old man. Vlasser went off without him."

Rather than face facts, I decided to go to bed. I tottered off to my room and undressed and then headed for the bathroom. Shrieking Eagle was taking a shower, so I went downstairs and brushed my teeth in the kitchen. When I got back to my room I took my bathrobe off and opened the closet to hang it up. El Toro snorted and bounced out. I shooed him out of the room, locked the door and sat down on the bed.

It was the last day of my bachelorhood and I had never felt worse in my life. It seemed as if I hadn't seen Sally for years and years, and between El Toro, Schuyler, Shrieking Eagle, Sugar Plum and all the Dudleys, not to mention the County Medical Officer, I was having serious misgivings about the morrow.

There was a knock at the door, and I got up and let Schuyler in. Here was a friend, rallying round to lend support. I needed it.

"Schuyler, old man . . ." I started.

Schuyler opened the closet. "Now where the hell has that goat gone? I need him."

"Schuyler, I—"

"He has to be driven off by Sherman's men. How the hell can I film *The March to the Sea* without a goat?"

"It's one o'clock in the morning, Schuyler. I'm getting married tomorrow. Good God—*today*. I need help. Knock off this damn picture, huh?"

"Sorry, boy. Weyman's about to touch off a big pile of wedding-present wrappers for the burning of Atlanta. He's got a big crowd of little boys for Joe Johnston's men falling back from the trenches, at a dime a head."

Schuyler disappeared.

I sat down on the bed again. I lit a cigarette. My hand was trembling.

Sugar Plum came in the door, looked around, and sniffed suspiciously at the closet. Then he walked over, laid his head on my knee, licked my hand and sighed.

I had a friend.

CHAPTER 10

MY wedding morning dawned bright and clear. I woke up with a start, and a great white goat with black spots, ridden by Shrieking Eagle in a cutaway and striped trousers, trotted silently into a dissolving dreamland. I listened. The house was quiet. Sugar Plum was asleep across the foot of my bed.

I looked over at the other bed.

Schuyler, fully dressed and puffing on a cigar, was lying on the covers. The bed was surrounded by camera equipment. Schuyler was frowning.

"Good morning," I said. "What time is it?"

"I think," Schuyler started slowly, "it would be better if she shot him right *after* the ceremony. More dramatic, don't you think?"

"Shoot who?"

"General Sherman, of course. Had to rewrite the whole damn script. Everybody quit on me at four o'clock."

I got up immediately, showered, shaved and dressed. It was around seven o'clock. In the kitchen I found a lot of new faces and a great deal of food, but nothing that looked like bacon and eggs. Someone pressed a chicken-salad sandwich in my hand, and I found some buttermilk standing unguarded in the refrigerator. I took these out on the kitchen stoop and sat down on the steps.

Daphne came around the corner of the house. She had a large sheaf of papers in her hands and was studying them industriously.

"Good morning," I said. "What is all that?"

"My lines," she said sleepily. "He said I had till nine o'clock to learn them."

I put the buttermilk and the sandwich down. Then I took the script out of her hands and put it in the garbage pail.

"Have you had breakfast?" I asked.

She shook her head. "I couldn't eat. Not today."

"That approach is reserved for the exclusive use of your sister. I've been reading up on weddings, and *you're* supposed to eat like a horse and smirk at everybody. If you don't like chicken salad, I shall perform minor surgery on one of the hams."

We went in. I turned over one of the hams and removed enough to feed both of us. We made sandwiches and went back out on the stoop.

"What's your schedule?" I asked.

"I'm supposed to help dress the bride," Daphne said, "but I can't wake her up. I tried."

"Well, you can come into Lye with me and collect my parents. I don't think I can find the way back all by myself."

We drove in, arrived just before the train, and managed to get my parents and their luggage off before it departed for High Point. The porter insisted that Lye was a freight stop. I pointed to my parents, standing beside me on the platform and brandishing baggage checks, and he finally capitulated, muttering, "I'll hear from the company about this."

My parents were prepared to greet everybody and everything with enthusiasm, but they sobered considerably on the drive to Bustard's Roost.

Father had a road map, which he kept inspecting, but after the Ay, Pee and Bee tracks he just folded the map and stared quietly out through a crack in the isinglass.

We stopped at the airport, and the proprietor greeted me.

"Any word from that jet yet?" I asked. It was still early, but I had no idea how far in advance these things had to be lined up.

"What jet?"

"An F-86. It's going to land here after lunch today."

"Here? A jet?"

"A jet. Here."

He scanned me closely. I looked perfectly sober. He finally snickered and wiped the counter.

"That's some Yankee Miss Sally's getting. A jet! Here!"

"Okay, okay," I said. "But you claim to be an airport, and by God you're getting business today. So you better get those cows off the runway. I'm warning you."

The proprietor whooped. He was enjoying himself thoroughly.

"I swear I don't know what the county's coming to. First I see an Indian. Chickasaw, too. Hasn't been one in these parts since the Black Hawk War. Then you tell me a jet's coming. All I need now is one of these motion-picture companies."

We drove off in a barrage of hoots.

A quarter of a mile from Bustard's Roost we passed Shrieking Eagle on Sally's mare Butterscotch. He had Sugar Plum and El Toro trotting at his heels, but even without them my parents would have stared in amazement. Shrieking Eagle's war bonnet was famous in Norfolk. He had counted coup eighty-four times, and it was the only war bonnet in the world with sea-gull feathers. The plain white feathers were Shore Patrolmen, and the eighteen feathers with red tips were grand coups and stood for Marines. There was one feather with a green tip, and while I wasn't absolutely certain, I always thought it represented the movie screen.

We reached Bustard's Roost, unloaded my parents, and introduced them all around. They were immediately grabbed off by Schuyler, who needed extras for the refugee scenes. Weyman materialized and informed me that two of Sally's ex-beaux were due after lunch and that Schuyler would then be put in protective custody.

We rescued my parents, so they could unpack. Father then presented me with two engagement rings and a note from the president of the company in Detroit asking, "Why didn't you say you knew Jack Weatherby?"

Then the mail arrived, with two more rings, but still no blood test. While we were considering the chances of telegraphing to Greenland, an armored car pulled in with a heavily insured package from Annapolis containing still another ring.

Around noon two yellow Cadillacs bumped up, and eight Indians got out. This group turned out to be Black Gold, Gushing, and Options Garfield, two of the lawyers, and three friends. They had been driving all night.

Schuyler saw them and his jaw dropped. He abandoned *The March to the Sea* and at once started to round up a cast for *She Rode with Custer*, but all the Indians had bedded down in the marquee which Shrieking Eagle had erected on the back lawn and they refused to come out. They were tired. Before he turned in, one of the lawyers presented me with their wedding gifts: a monogrammed tomahawk for me and a small deerskin medicine pouch for Sally. As soon as the lawyer was out of sight, Daphne snatched the pouch away from me, wrapped it in aluminum foil and locked it in a drawer.

"Watch it," she whispered. "That stuff's dynamite. Fertility powder."

Nobody wanted any lunch, and everybody wanted a nap before the goings-on started. I couldn't sleep, so I wandered around the house and brooded. The two ex-beaux showed up, both over six feet three and wearing faultlessly crumpled linen suits. Weyman greeted them and took them aside to talk to them. Both of them nodded, and in a twinkling they, Schuyler and the movie equipment were all out of sight.

I wandered into the parlor and tried to assimilate the fact that under this very roof, in this very room, my bachelorhood was within a few hours to be terminated. It was getting harder and harder to realize.

All the furniture except the piano had been cleared out, and the potted palms had clustered together on either side of the fireplace. Directly over the mantelpiece hung a picture of Dudley Stubblefield, dated 1866. Whatever he had done at the Battle of Little Hominy had cost him part of his right ear, and he looked as if I weren't pulling any wool over *his* eyes. He obviously knew all about my great-uncle.

A few people still drifted through the house carrying punch bowls, flowers and hams. There were noises upstairs, as if the masses were bestirring themselves. On an impulse I checked on the two ex-beaux. They were out in the rose garden, teaching Schuyler just how a mint leaf should be bruised for a julep. All the samples he turned over for inspection were either bruised too hard or not enough, and they made him keep on trying.

Cousin Bob arrived and started to set up shop in front

of the fireplace. I introduced myself, but he only nodded briefly and went on with the assembly of his portable altar.

A small party left for the airport to collect Jimmy. No one was paying any attention to anyone else, and I got the impression that if a latter-day Lochinvar had suddenly appeared at this point, he could have gotten Sally halfway to Saskatchewan before anyone knew she was gone.

Guests were starting to arrive, so I ate half an apple and retired to change.

I dressed very carefully. I was, after all, the groom, and the honor of the North rested on my shoulders. It was my own wedding, and now if ever was the time to cut a sartorial swathe. I even had a sword, borrowed from Rudolph, and Captain O'Gara had lent me a golden sword knot.

I got into my whites and reached into the closet for my shoes. El Toro, I found, had been there before me. Both my white shoes, and one of Schuyler's, had been reduced to a pulp.

I put on Schuyler's shoe, got out the white polish, and proceeded to convert a black shoe. After about six coats the original shade was barely noticeable, so long as I kept my right foot forward.

I buttoned my coat, opened the bureau drawer, got out a pair of gloves, unrolled them, and found the right one was a sock. There was another note from Schuyler.

The final result, if I say so myself, was little short of

resplendent. I was nothing to disgrace the ghost of David Glasgow Farragut, and a fig for Dudley Stubblefield.

With half an hour to go, I wandered out to the front hall. There was an air of determined intensity in the parlor. The two ex-beaux had finally accepted one of the mint leaves, and Schuyler had suggested that since they had such a large number of them, perhaps a julep might be in order. All three of them were sitting in a corner singing "The Wind Blew the Bonnie Lassie's Plaidie Awa'," and they sounded as if they were good for hours.

There were signs of life from under the marquee, and Cousin Bob was synchronizing watches with Weyman and two small boys. A small girl carrying a vase filled with roses bumped into me, piped "Watch it, Mac," and hurried into the kitchen. Guests were milling around and chatting happily.

A small, rotund man, who turned out to be the County Medical Officer, buttonholed me, waggled a finger under my nose, whispered "Don't forget," and retired behind one of the groups of potted palms behind the altar. There was a squeal, and El Toro emerged, glared over his shoulder, and retired behind the other group. Sugar Plum trotted in, with a large red bow in his collar, glanced off Cousin Bob, and then scrabbled in behind the group sheltering El Toro.

Schuyler had moved to the piano, and a number of guests gathered around. Most of them had juleps, and after a few minutes they started "The Yellow Rose of Texas."

Suddenly the tent flap opened, and all nine Indians marched out in single file. They stalked into the living room and dressed ranks in front of the piano.

With exactly four minutes to go, a station wagon pulled up at the front door. From it debarked my parents, Daphne, two Dudleys, and a tall unshaven figure in a sweat-stained flying suit with pencils and knives and slide rules sticking out of little pockets.

The outline of a MIG was stenciled on the back of the flying suit, with a large red X painted over it. Under this was stenciled "GO—TIGER." It was a little hard to read, because there was a parachute slung over one shoulder. My father was carrying a clothes bag, and Mother had a crash helmet with black and orange stripes. Daphne was carrying an oxygen mask.

"Sorry, old man. Couldn't change in the car. Say, that's a hell of a small field. Had to buzz it twice to clear the cows. Manager had a stroke or something. Can I get a drink before the show starts?"

My moral support had arrived.

Someone stuck his head down the stairs and whistled shrilly. "The Yellow Rose of Texas" faded out raggedly, and the Wedding March started. A foot in the small of my back propelled me violently toward the fireplace, and I crashed into a potted palm. There was a low growl, and a bleat, and the palm rocked and settled. Cousin Bob cleared his throat and looked out at the audience. I saw Sally starting down the stairs. A long arm emerged from behind the other group of palms and a hand settled on Cousin Bob's shoulder. Just before Sally got to the bottom of the stairs, Weyman squeaked into the living room ahead of her and thrust an envelope into my hand. It had a Greenland APO postmark. I passed it across to the hand on Cousin Bob's shoulder and the hand withdrew.

The guests were quieting down, although over the Wedding March you could still hear a mutter of "Should have seen those cows move. . . . Fourteen MIGs, wasn't it? . . . Right to the end of the runway. . . . Just bringing the manager to . . . Morocco tomorrow morning . . ."

The ceremony was no strain for the groom. Sally was beautiful, and when I looked at her everything else faded into the background, even the rasping noises around my feet. I said "I will!" so firmly that Cousin Bob reared back, and when I was asked for a ring I held out a whole handful, clutched in a white sock. Cousin Bob picked one out, and while he was blessing it I got the sock off and put the other rings in it and dropped them into the potted palm.

And I did kiss the bride. I did.

A whole passel of people kissed the bride, and one of the ex-beaux got around to it three times. Some people even kissed the groom. I had a good deal of lipstick on my whites before it was all over, and Jimmy even got some on his MIG. The kissing didn't really die down until Shrieking Eagle entered the arena, leaving war paint all down the line.

We moved out to the marquee for the reception, and I was given a glass of champagne which I never got to drink.

One of the beaux grabbed me by the elbow. He was on his third julep.

"If you're not good to that li'l gal, I'll break every bone in your body," he growled through set teeth.

"Stick to your mint, Buster," I started.

Sally came up and separated us.

"Thomas Lea, you go take some ham biscuits to your aunt. March, now."

She leaned over to wipe some lipstick off me.

"Never mind Thomas Lea. He's said that to every groom about every girl that's been married down here since he was fourteen years old."

The congratulations, which had slowed down while the champagne was being poured, started in again. Sally and I stood back to back and shook hundreds of hands. Then we posed for pictures. It was only much later, in looking over the results, that I realized Sugar Plum had licked the black shoe clean during the ceremony, while El Toro was eating the sword knot.

Daphne came up to me with Shrieking Eagle.

"He's a genuine shaman," she said, her eyes shining happily. "They're going to do a Rain Dance so that I can write my honors paper on it."

There was a tiny cloud over by the airport, no bigger than a man's hand, and I wanted it to stay that way.

"Now look here," I started, but Daphne dragged him off, chatting happily in Chickasaw.

Sally went upstairs to change, and I fought my way back to my room. Three very pretty girls were resting there with their shoes off, drinking champagne out of coffee cups, and I had to go into the closet to change. Schuyler had evidently taken my brown shoes, so I left on my honeymoon in bedroom slippers.

I got out to the car and had the windows closed before the rice barrage started. Sally's mother slipped two bottles of champagne into the back, and Sally appeared in a ravishing black-and-white dress and with a paper plate full of shrimps in her hands, and we ducked into the car.

Just as I closed the door I heard a piercing yell from behind the house. I looked up and saw the Garfields, arms flung over their heads, singing a guttural chant and jogging heavily from one foot to the other. Daphne stood near them, hands clasped in admiration and a large notebook under one arm. Schuyler already had his camera set up and was grinding away.

By the time we reached Big Hominy it was coming down in sheets.

"He does come in handy, sometimes," Sally said, popping the last of the shrimps into her mouth and dropping the paper plate over into the back seat. I put the remark down to bridal confusion until I heard a gentle grinding from the rear of the car. El Toro was munching up the plate.

At the Albemarle Inn in Charlottesville we did our best to act as if we were old hands at this sort of thing. The act had even less success than it normally does, what with El Toro and the champagne bottles. As I was signing in, I took off a bedroom slipper to shake out some rice, and laid it on the desk. The manager shifted it carefully to one side and smiled blandly at me. Tapping a bell, he bawled "Bridal Suite!" and our caravan crossed the lobby. Three bellboys came in with us, and I gave one five dollars to take El Toro away and another one ten dollars to go get me some shoes.

Finally even these people disappeared, and Sally and I were alone at last.

We were *married*.

Sally moved her suitcase into the bedroom and looked around. Then she came out and sat down and started to comb the rice out of her hair. I stood there in my slippers holding the champagne bottles and watched her.

She looked so sweet, so lovely, so innocent.

She looked up, saw me, smiled tenderly. She spoke to me softly.

"There's no icebox in here, darling. Put the champagne bottles in the john, will you?"

I was a Brown Bagger.

ABOUT THE AUTHOR

Of the 410 men in his graduating class at the United States Naval Academy, Donald R. Morris stood 1st in Naval History and 409th in Electrical Engineering. He claims for himself the distinction of having been the only midshipman in history to complete the four-year course without finding out what a cosine was.

Since graduation Lieutenant Morris has served in various destroyers, LSTs, and in Public Information. He also spent nine months in the Naval School of Languages, studying Russian. According to his calculations, it cost the United States government $5.86 for every Russian word he learned. The only word he remembers that is worth anything near this amount is "Vweesokoprevostkhodeetyelstvo," which means "Sir."

Lieutenant Morris was born in 1924 and raised in New York City. He has been in the Navy fifteen years, and it is beginning to look like a steady occupation. He is currently assigned to the Bureau of Naval Personnel and has never had an opportunity to say "Vweesokoprevostkhodeety-elstvo."

His previously published works include China Station, *a novel, and articles for* The Atlantic Monthly, True, Argosy, Naval Institute Proceedings, *and other periodicals.*

He is married and has two small children, and we have no idea how he finds time to write. But we are grateful he does. The same, Vweesokoprevostkhodeetyelstvo or Madam, will go for you.